No. 485
$7.95

HOW TO USE TEST INSTRUMENTS IN ELECTRONICS SERVICING

By Fred Shunaman

TAB BOOKS

BLUE RIDGE SUMMIT, PA. 17214

FIRST EDITION

FIRST PRINTING — APRIL 1970

Copyright © 1970 by TAB BOOKS

Printed in the United States
of America

Library of Congress Card Number: 68-21593

Preface

The technician or experimenter often asks: What can a DC scope, or a capacitance checker, or a color-bar generator do for me? The answer is simple. Test instruments can't do anything for you, but you can do things with test instruments. You are the one who diagnoses the trouble and repairs the equipment. The more instruments you have—and know how to use —the easier your work and the more of it you can do. And you can find out things with the help of instruments that you would never have known otherwise.

Test instruments give you information and your brain interprets that information, but one further source of data is necessary. You need service manuals and schematics on the equipment you are servicing. True, most TV sets resemble most others. Obviously, if they differed widely from the norm they just wouldn't work! So a schematic of one will give you an idea of how most others are designed. But from a practical point of view, it is precisely the individual differences that count! One kind of horizontal oscillator in a TV set will give you a waveform that would look all wrong if you were expecting to find another type of oscillator. And if you find a completely burned-up resistor, the schematic will tell you exactly what its value was. (And there are some surprising differences between component values in different sets.)

Now you have three things: fixed data, instruments (to obtain variable data) and the brain to use them. You have to interpret your meter and scope indications, combine them, determine by reference to the fixed data if they indicate something wrong, then test your decision. If it isn't the answer, or the complete answer, you have to gather more information, correlate it with what you already have, and test another decision. The accuracy of your decision will depend on three things: The quality and versatility of your instruments (how much they can tell you), the availability of fixed data (service information), and the supply of data you have in your head (your knowledge of the equipment being tested and of your test equipment). <u>The more you know about your instruments, the more you can do with them,</u> and the more valuable they can be to you.

Permit me to express my appreciation to Amphenol Cadre Division, Hichok, and Sencore for photograph. Also to Allied Radio, B&K Division of Dynascon, EICO, Earl Brothers of Heath, J.W. Bosiger of Seco and Sidney Chertok of Sprague for their assistance with technical and pictorial data.

Table of Contents

CHAPTER 1

The Oscilloscope

Without a doubt, the service technician's most useful instrument is the oscilloscope (or just "scope"). Just what is the scope and why is it so useful? When you come right down to it, the scope is nothing more than a voltmeter, but it can tell you the voltage in a circuit at any instant of time. It's that any instant of time that makes the scope important! It makes the scope different from any other voltmeter. It adds a dimension we don't have in any other instrument—the dimension of time! Because of that, the scope can tell you not only how much voltage you have in a circuit, but what kind of voltage. You know whether you have sine, square-wave or pulse waveforms—and if pulses, what type. The scope makes this possible because you can see the voltage at each instant instead of its lumped-up result such as presented by a pointer-type voltmeter. Ordinary voltmeters may be calibrated in RMS, peak, or even average voltages. The scope can give you all three—simultaneously!

THE SCOPE AS A VOLTMETER

The scope is a voltmeter whose pointer (or indicator) is a beam of electrons that make a point or spot of light at the center of the screen when it is at rest. Apply a voltage to the vertical input terminals and the beam will move or deflect. The spot rises above (or drops below) the center line. The scope also has internal circuitry that sweeps the spot horizontally across the screen at various desired rates. So if you want to check the ordinary 60-Hz (Hz is the abbreviation for cps) electric power line, you set the horizontal control so the spot sweeps across the screen 60 times a second and connect the vertical input terminals to the AC line.

Now the spot is moved vertically by the applied AC voltage

as it is swept horizontally across the screen by the sweep circuits in the scope. It sweeps across the screen once for every cycle (1/60 second) of the 60-Hz current, flips back almost instantaneously to where it began, and starts out again to follow the voltage through the next cycle. What you see is a series of traces, one over the other, so they look like a single trace. The trace shows you that the AC line voltage starts out from zero, rises to its full voltage during the first half cycle, drops back again to zero, changes direction, rises to its maximum voltage in the other direction and returns to zero again in the second half of the cycle. This shows you that the AC waveform looks just like the curves in the textbook!

Not only can the scope show the true pattern of the waveform from the AC power line, but it can do the same thing for all complex waves, the signals and pulses that go through your TV set. And not only TV! With the help of a square-wave generator you can find out—almost instantly—how good a hi-fi amplifier is. You are able to compare special types of signals—sync pulses at various stages in the TV circuitry, for example—with signals at the same points in known-good equipment (or as a second best, with those in the service manual). Thus you can see immediately where a signal is going wrong.

Not only will the scope show you where a signal is being lost or distorted (possibly in a stage where all DC voltages are correct) but it will reveal any signals that are not supposed to be there—for instance, pulses in the supposedly pure DC power supply. Of course, if a supply is really pure DC it should show nothing on an AC scope and a straight line on a DC one. If the supply does show pulses it may be a warning of a leaky filter capacitor.

The scope offers a few other advantages that are unique. The "pointer" beam swings up in nanoseconds, and doesn't overshoot. And you can't overload it. (It shares that advantage with the VTVM, of course.) If you have a high-grade scope you can measure the exact width (time period) of your pulses, a decided advantage in some kinds of industrial servicing.

INTERPRETING WHAT YOU SEE

You never quite get something for nothing, and the scope gives the average technician one great problem. He has to interpret the indications he sees on its face. (Actually, this is true about any voltmeter, but it's much easier to take the VOM literally.) For instance, you may have a signal that looks much like the sine wave you get from the electric power line but with a sharp, high pulse at one side, as shown in Fig. 1-1. Now you have to stop and ask yourself a few questions. What is causing the pulse? What is it doing to the following circuitry? Is it the cause of the trouble you are chasing? Had you been measuring the same voltage with a VTVM and found it a few volts high, you might have suspected some spurious signal, but the chances are 9 to 1 that you would have passed it off as due to component tolerances. So, the necessity of interpreting your readings is an advantage, not a disadvantage, even though it does add a complicating factor. You are much better off when you can see some out-of-the-way thing and have to interpret it than you would be if you didn't know it was there.

Compared to an ordinary VTVM, a scope has a few more controls. We are used to centering (or zero-setting) the indicator on a voltmeter or ohmmeter. But the scope's indicator—the spot—moves in two directions, so we need two centering controls, one vertical and one horizontal. And, since the pointer is a beam of electrons, we need a control to brighten it so all of the waveform can be seen. And even more important, we need to be able to dim it again when a bright spot isn't needed.

TWO KINDS OF SCOPES

Oscilloscopes are divided roughly into service and professional (or laboratory) types, while some fall between the two classes. A few extremely high-class types are found only in the better-equipped or specialized laboratories. The service

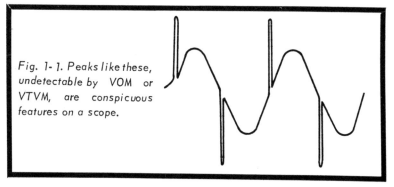

Fig. 1-1. Peaks like these, undetectable by VOM or VTVM, are conspicuous features on a scope.

scope is generally an AC type—that is, it uses amplifiers with blocking capacitors in the grid circuits. Therefore, it will not measure DC and may fall off a little when measuring AC at low frequencies. The professional scope is invariably a DC type and has amplifiers engineered to be accurate from DC up into the megahertz range.

The lab scope has other important features, too. The sweep circuits of a service scope are calibrated roughly in Hertz (cycles per second). You set the frequency selector at, say, 5,000 (Hz) and find frequencies between 2,500 and 25,000 with the vernier frequency adjustment. Calibration of the professional scope is exact, usually in microseconds per centimeter. Thus, the professional scope can be used to measure the rise time of an audio transient, for instance. To measure rise time, pulse width, etc., it is convenient to be able to start them at a zero point. To accomplish this action, the professional scope is triggered; in other words, the pulse or other signal to be measured starts the sweep. This is the third important feature of the professional scope.

Naming these features doesn't really point out all the differences between a medium- and high-quality scope. Reliability and accuracy are built into the professional scope to a greater extent. A laboratory scope amplifier may be rated for roughly the same sensitivity and rise time as the amplifier is a medium-quality instrument, yet use twice as many tubes to achieve the desired linearity and gain. Attenuators are engineered for much greater accuracy and better shielding, and a great deal of work is done to make calibration more exact and dependable over longer periods of time than in less expensive instruments.

SCOPE CONTROLS

The AC scope is by far the most common type. Fig. 1-2 can be taken (with some variation) to represent practically any of the better medium-priced scopes that would likely be used in TV and similar servicing work. (DC scopes are a little more complicated, but some of the controls may be duplicated on AC models).

The first—top—control is marked INTEN. Besides turning the scope on and off, it controls the spot's brightness, or intensity. (The rule is to never turn the brightness up more than necessary. Too bright a spot may burn the screen, especially if it rests in one place.) The control below it, FOCUS, sharpens the spot to a pinpoint; it does roughly the same thing as the focus control on a TV set. The two zero-centering adjustments, vertical and horizontal position, VERT POS, HOR POS, are just below it.

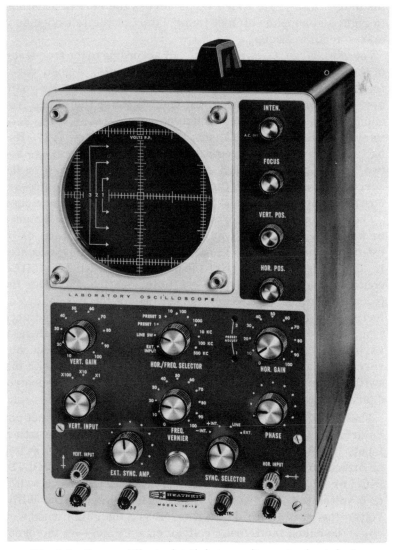

Fig. 1-2. Scopes differ in detail, but a medium-priced unit looks much like this one.

The horizontal frequency selector, FREQ SEL, controls the frequency of a small variable-frequency oscillator whose output moves the spot horizontally across the screen. The voltage across the horizontal deflecting plates in the scope cathode-ray tube rises gradually during the first half of each cycle from the sawtooth oscillator, then drops back to zero almost instantly. Thus, the spot sweeps across the screen from left to right and appears almost immediately at the left edge as it starts another sweep.

You can change the sweep frequency according to the frequency of the voltage you want to study. For example, a good sweep frequency for a 60 Hz-voltage is 30 or 60 Hz. At 30 Hz you'll see two sine waves; at 60 just one, because the sweep frequency is the same as the voltage you're measuring. To check many waveforms in a TV set, the scope is set to 7,875 Hz, half the TV's line sweep rate of 15,750 Hz. Thus, we see two "fields" (two horizontal scan lines of the TV signal) on the screen. Some scopes (and other instruments) have pre-set control positions at 30 and 7,875 Hz to speed up TV servicing.

The horizontal gain control, HOR GAIN, sets the distance or width the spot is driven by the internal oscillator, or by external signals applied to the HOR INPUT terminals located in the lower right corner of the panel. The FREQ VERNIER control "tunes" the internal oscillator continuously over the frequency ranges between the settings of the frequency selector. The oscillator is usually a resistance-capacitance type; the frequency selector simply switches in capacitors of various sizes for rough frequency variation. The frequency vernier is a variable resistor that, in conjunction with the switched capacitors, provides continuous frequency control over the range selected by each fixed capacitor.

The VERT GAIN adjusts the distance or height the spot can be driven up or down by a voltage connected to the vertical input, VERT, terminals. The VERT INPUT ATTEN switch or attenuator below it is a multiplier usually marked VOLTS/INCH or X1, X10, X100. It is equivalent to the range switch on a voltmeter. For a very small input voltage (a few millivolts) the switch would be set on X1 and the gain turned well up. To check the flyback voltage on a TV set—in the order of thousands of volts—the input voltage is first attenuated by clipping the scope probe to the outside of the insulation on the horizontal output tube's anode lead. The attenuator switch is then set to X100 and the gain control turned well down. The input attenuator on most scopes is not designed for the voltages encountered in TV horizontal output and high-voltage systems. A direct connection would damage the input circuits.

There are two other important controls on most scopes in the medium-priced class—the sync selector and sync amplitude controls, SYNC SEL and SYNC AMP. To know what an AC voltage is doing at all times during the cycle we have to sweep the spot across the screen at the right speed. We have to keep it in time—in sync with the measured voltage—but we don't have to sweep at the same frequency as the measured voltage. If we sweep at exactly half the frequency, we will get two cycles on the screen; at one-third the frequency, three cycles, etc.

For "60-cycle" voltages there is no problem; just control the horizontal travel of the spot with a signal from the 60-Hz power line that is no doubt also supplying the voltage we are measuring. All we have to do is turn the frequency selector to LINE SWITCH (Fig. 1-3). Now the horizontal sweep is being supplied by the 60-Hz AC line and the scope's internal oscillator is not used. If we turn the frequency selector to some other frequency and leave the SYNC SEL on LINE we can sweep

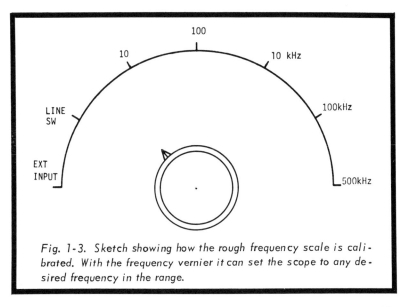

Fig. 1-3. Sketch showing how the rough frequency scale is calibrated. With the frequency vernier it can set the scope to any desired frequency in the range.

at various frequencies, but those at a multiple of 60 Hz will be the most stable because synchronization occurs at 60 Hz. Be setting the frequency selector at EXT INPUT we disconnect the internal oscillator and draw a horizontal sweep voltage from an external source. This function is especially useful when we want to take our sync signal from the voltage being measured. The Sync SEL switch has a position for selecting an external sync source as well, through the EXT SYNC terminal on the panel. The other positions, plus INT and minus INT are used to provide internal synchronization by feeding back a little of the signal voltage from the vertical amplifier to keep the sweep in step with the input signal.

Thus, we can proceed in more than one way to measure some voltages: We can sweep the scope screen with the internal oscillator and provide sync with either the feedback (INT SYNC), the 60-Hz line, or the input signal voltage itself through the external sync terminal. We can also use the input signal to supply horizontal as well as vertical deflection, making sync automatic and absolute. The SYNC AMP is a gain control that sets the amount of sync voltage fed back to the sweep generator. The PHASE control is used to start the horizontal sweep at the same instant as the measured voltage starts its vertical deflection; in other words, it keeps the vertical and horizontal deflection signals in step, or phase.

USING THE SCOPE

The fantastic number of possible uses for the scope makes it impossible to do more than point out the main applications here. (Numerous books are devoted entirely to the subject including Oscilloscope Techniques and 101 Ways to Use Your Scope. Some books such as Using Your Scope in Audio Service, The Scope in Industrial Service, and many more deal with more specialized uses.) By far the most common scope uses are analyzing waveforms and tracing signals in TV. These are covered in Chapter 2.

The oscilloscope, regardless of its type, is designed to provide a visual pattern of a signal. Some of the more common types are the general-purpose AC, wideband and dual-trace scopes. The general-purpose scope is useful for servicing B/W TV and many industrial circuits. For these applications an AC scope with a 500-kHz vertical bandwidth will usually fill the needs. However, for servicing more complex circuits, such as found in today's modern stereo FM multiplex receivers, color TV, and communications equipment, the wideband scope is used. A wideband scope has a much wider vertical bandwidth, usually up to 5 MHz or more. The oscilloscope lets you examine the characteristics of a waveform for shape, amplitude, frequency, and phase. A voltage can be shown as a vertical displacement on a horizontal sweep or time base, or it can be compared with another voltage by using both the vertical and horizontal inputs.

SCOPE GRATICULES

In order to measure an input waveform level on a scope, there has to be some means of reference and calibration. To accomplish this, oscilloscopes have an overlay screen on the face of the CRT. This screen is called a "graticule." Some graticules consist of ruled vertical and horizontal lines printed on a sheet of plexiglass and held to the CRT face by a panel cover (see Fig. 1-2).

The graticule divisions are also often referred to as the "X"

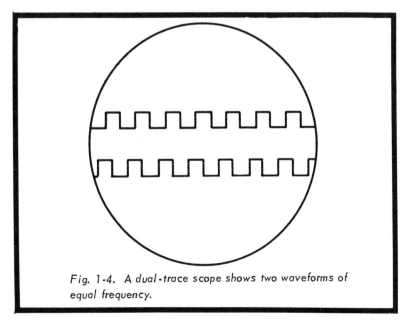

Fig. 1-4. A dual-trace scope shows two waveforms of equal frequency.

and "Y" axis; the vertical amplitude is the "Y" axis and horizontal is the "X" axis. The scope face is behind the graticule, of course, so you are viewing traces through the graticule, which may not always be desirable. So another type of graticule became popular. This type has etched lines which are visible only when illuminated by a special lighting arrangement. A control is normally provided to set the brightness of the lines as desired.

SCOPE CALIBRATION

If the scope is used to simply view a waveform without regard to its level or value, calibration is not necessary. But when using the scope for measurement of voltage, it must be calibrated with a known value. Some scopes provide an internal calibration source, while others rely on an external value. In either case, the calibrating voltage is applied to the scope's vertical input and the controls adjusted to provide a specific amplitude on the graticule. For example: supposing our calibrating source is a 6v AC sine wave from a filament transformer. We would connect it to the vertical input and adjust the controls to center the waveform as well as setting the amplitude so that the peak-to-peak points fill out an even number of divisions on the graticule. Remember too that a scope reads in peak-to-peak values and the calibrating voltage must be a peak-to-peak value. If it is not, it can be converted as follows:

If the calibration source is:	Convert to peak-to-peak by multiplying by
RMS	2.83
Peak	2.0
Average	1.27

Since the 6v AC calibrating sine wave is an RMS value, we must multiply it by 2.83 to get the peak-to-peak amplitude. In this case, 6 X 2.83 equals 16.98 which we can round off to 17 volts to make calibration easier. If our input sine wave is adjusted to fill 17 divisions, then each division is equal to

16

one volt. The scope sweep rate should be set to allow at least two complete waveforms.

AC MEASUREMENTS

Now that you have the scope calibrated to measure one volt per graticule division, leave all the controls just as they are and remove the calibration signal. Connect your test probe to the vertical input and proceed to make your voltage measurement. If you are measuring with anything other than a direct probe, be sure to figure in the probe loss. For example, if your measuring probe has a 10-to-1 attenuation factor, your reading on the scope graticule must be multiplied by 10 to compensate for this reduction. Let's assume we are using a low-capacity probe with 10-to-1 attenuation and the amplitude of the measured signal reads six divisions (three above and three below the zero reference line). Since each division represents 1 volt, we have a 6-volt peak-to-peak waveform which multiplied by 10 equals 60 volts peak to peak!

Suppose we make the same measurement using a direct probe having no attenuation. Since our scope is calibrated only to 17 volts peak to peak, the input voltage would be too high to read. To compensate for this, all scopes have an input attenuator switch. It may be calibrated to read in volts per division; it may simply say VERTICAL ATTEN with positions labeled X1, X10, and X100. These attenuators do about the same thing as the range switch on a voltmeter. By switching the scope vertical attenuator to the X10 (times 10) position, all readings on the graticule are reduced by a factor of 10 times. Simply multiply by 10 to get the correct reading. Any time the scope attenuation is changed from what it was during calibration, the new attenuation factor must be applied to find the correct amplitude or level of the input voltage. If both the vertical attenuator and an attenuated probe are used, these factors must be considered to obtain the correct voltage measurement.

DC MEASUREMENTS

Measuring a DC voltage is much the same as measuring AC, except that the scope trace (with no input) is set to a zero reference line with the vertical position control. Assuming the scope has been calibrated, the DC measurement is now

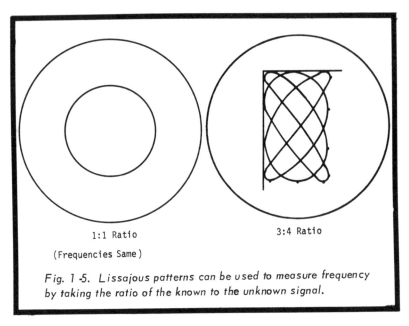

1:1 Ratio

(Frequencies Same)

3:4 Ratio

Fig. 1-5. Lissajous patterns can be used to measure frequency by taking the ratio of the known to the unknown signal.

read in the same manner as AC. As an example, the scope is calibrated to read one volt per division as before. With an input signal, set the scope trace to a zero reference line. This may be the bottom line on the graticule if the measured voltage is positive or the top line of the graticule if the measured voltage is to be negative. Since our scope graticule has 17 divisions, we can measure 0 to 17 volts DC directly and higher using the attenuator as described in AC measurements.

FREQUENCY MEASUREMENTS

There are several ways an oscilloscope can be used to measure an unknown frequency, depending on the type of scope. Dual-trace scopes or a scope with an external electronic switch can be used by feeding a known frequency from a signal generator to one input (Channel A) and the unknown frequency to the other input (Channel B). Then simply adjust the signal generator (unknown) until the two signals are equal and read the frequency from the generator. This is also sometimes referred to as a comparison method.

Another method is based on frequency ratio between two signals, one known and one unknown. This provides a "lissajous" pattern (see Fig. 1-5). In this method, the known frequency is fed to the horizontal input and the "unknown" fed to the vertical input. As shown, the vertical "X" axis is across the top of the waveform and the horizontal "Y" axis is along the left side of the waveform. In the illustration, four loops of the horizontal wave touch the "Y" axis and three touch the vertical "X" axis. This means the ratio between the signals is 3:4. The vertical frequency is three-fourths of the horizontal frequency. Assuming our horizontal (known) frequency is 400 Hz, the vertical (unknown) frequency is 3/4 x 400 or 300 Hz.

MEASURING PHASE SHIFT

Another common use of a scope is measuring phase shift, again using lissajous patterns. For example, suppose we want to test an audio amplifier. The connections are made as shown in Fig. 1-6 so that the same generator is supplying the horizontal sweep (through the amplifier) and the vertical deflection. If amplification is perfect, the lissajous pattern will be a diagonal line as shown in Fig. 1-7A. Various forms of distortion may be spotted immediately as indicated in the illustration. To measure phase shift through an amplifier, both the audio generator output and the amplifier input are connected to the scope's input terminals. The output of the

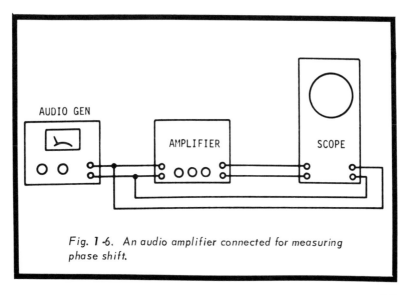

Fig. 1-6. An audio amplifier connected for measuring phase shift.

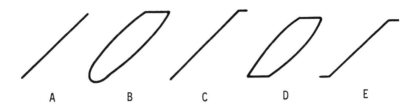

A   B   C   D   E

A--excellent response
B--phase shift, positive clipping
C--clipping; no phase shift
D--positive and negative clipping plus phase shift
E--positive and negative clipping, no phase shift

Fig. 1-7. *Some things the scope can tell you: A — excellent response; B — phase shift, positive clipping; C — clipping, no phase shift; D — phase shift added to positive and negative clipping; E — clipping at both ends without phase shift.*

amplifier is connected to the scope's horizontal input terminals as in Fig. 1-6. Any departure from phase linearity opens the diagonal line into an ellipse.

CHAPTER 2

Servicing With the Scope

Some technicians shy away from the scope simply because they don't understand the waveforms they see or know how to derive any meaning from them. An unfortunate situation, indeed, because a scope can be his eyes that enable him to peer into a maze of components and determine what is or isn't happening.

In audio work a scope is generally used with a square-wave generator, for example, to determine distortion in a hi-fi amplifier as shown in Fig. 2-1. But the scope really becomes useful in servicing the more complicated circuits found in television receivers. The vast number of waveforms, the importance of their specific patterns and amplitude, make the scope the only effective diagnostic instrument. The purpose here is to explore the possibilities and procedures as they relate to TV troubles. We will assume before we start that tubes have been checked and replaced if necessary. A scope is of the greatest help in isolating a problem to a particular stage. After that, a voltmeter or ohmmeter can be used to check circuit voltages and isolate the problem to a defective component. Before you start to service anything, it's a good practice to get the manufacturer's service manual and schematic. You need this "road map" as a guide to tell you what the correct voltages should be.

LOCATING TV TROUBLES

There are a few major points in using a scope that should be considered. The first, of course, is to understand your scope, how it works, and how to use it. The second is to know what the normal waveform should look like. For the applications here we are concerned with three types of probes: direct, low-capacitance, and demodulator (or RF). The di-

Fig. 2-1. *Square waves reveal a boost in low frequencies (A), a low-frequency loss (B), a sharp drop-off of high frequencies (C), and oscillation or ringing (D).*

rect probe is used when you are not concerned with circuit loading—in the audio stages, for example. A low-capacitance probe is used in critical circuits where the scope itself may affect circuit operation such as the sync, video detector, AGC, vertical, and horizontal oscillator stages. One important thing to remember about a low-capacitance probe is that it reduces the input signal to the scope by 10 to 1. For example: a 100-volt signal will appear as a 10-volt signal to the scope. The demodulator probe actually has a built-in detector circuit to view signals in the IF and RF stages.

No Raster- Sound Normal

This relatively common symptom tells you right away that everything up to the pix detector is normal since you have normal sound. Naturally, the first thing you want to check is the fuse in the high-voltage section. If the fuse is OK, check for high voltage by holding a screwdriver—with an insulated handle—near the pix tube anode. You should draw an arc. If you have high voltage, check the pix tube socket for loose or broken connections; also check the brightness control. If there is no arc (or a very small one) after checking the high-voltage rectifier, the horizontal sweep circuits probably are at fault. Connect the scope through a low-capacitance probe to the grid of the horizontal output tube, Point B in Fig. 2-2. The frequency of the horizontal oscillator is 15,750 Hz so the scope sweep should be set at one-half this frequency to view at least two cycles of the waveform. The grid signal should be negative and the amplitude close to that specified by the manufacturer. You should see a pattern similar to that shown in Fig. 2-3. If normal, turn the set off and connect the probe to the insulation of the horizontal plate lead—Point A in Fig. 2-2. The normal waveform here is shown in Fig. 2-4. Be careful—you're near high voltage!

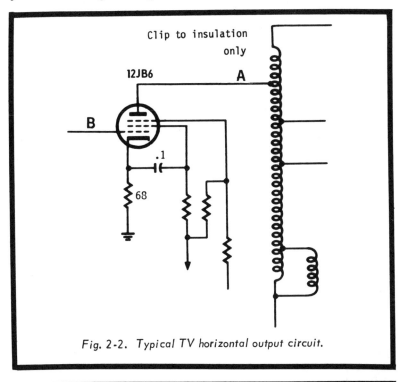

Clip to insulation
only

12JB6   A

B

.1

68

Fig. 2-2. Typical TV horizontal output circuit.

Fig. 2-3. The waveform on the horizontal output grid should resemble the one shown.

Fig. 2-4. This waveform is typical of that appearing with the scope lead clipped to the insulated horizontal output lead.

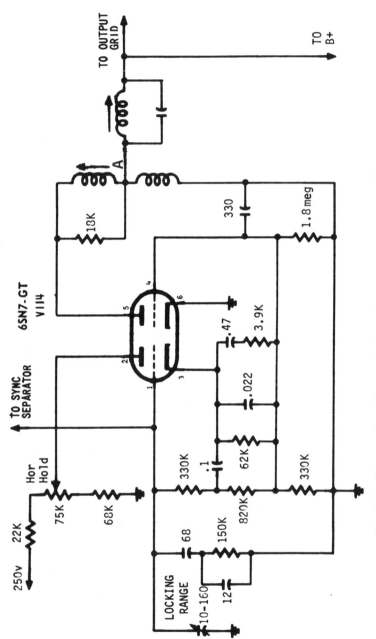

Fig. 2-5. The synchroguide circuit is used in many horizontal oscillator stages.

24

If the waveform at the grid was normal but not at the plate, you have isolated the problem to the horizontal output and it is time to get out the multimeter to check voltage and resistance (we assume that the tube was substituted first). If the grid waveform was not normal, move the scope probe to the horizontal oscillator output. Fig. 2-5 shows the well-known synchroguide oscillator circuit. The output waveform taken at Point A is shown in Fig. 2-6. We are using the scope to iso-

Fig. 2-6. Waveform appearing at Point A in Fig. 2-5.

late the defect to a stage or circuit, remember. Low grid drive to the horizontal output tube traced to low output from the oscillator can be caused by low oscillator plate voltage. Again, check the scope waveform for normal amplitude as well as for normal waveshape. A low-capacitance probe must be used in these circuits. A direct probe will upset such circuits and result in inaccurate waveforms.

Transistorized circuits vary from the older tube designs as shown by the partial RCA KCS153 chassis schematic in Fig. 2-7. The waveforms taken at various test points in this cir-

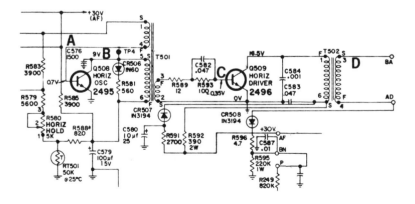

Fig. 2-7. Horizontal oscillator circuit used in RCA KCS153 chassis.

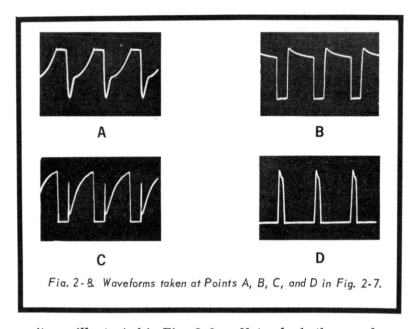

Fia. 2-8. Waveforms taken at Points A, B, C, and D in Fig. 2-7.

cuit are illustrated in Fig. 2-8. Not only do the waveforms differ from those of tube-type circuits, but from those of other transistorized sweep circuits. Fig. 2-9 shows the same portion of a Sylvania A01 chassis which uses a multivibrator-type circuit. The waveforms in this circuit are illustrated in Fig. 2-10. Notice that only the horizontal output waveform is similar to those of other circuits. When servicing transistorized horizontal circuits you will see that an amplifier is used (horizontal driver in Fig. 2-7) between the oscillator and output stages to boost the driving voltage. If you have a problem in these circuits, it is wise to check the bias on the output transistor base first.

HORIZONTAL AND HIGH-VOLTAGE CIRCUITS

The schematic diagram of Fig. 2-11 shows the horizontal and high-voltage circuits of a Setchell Carlson Model 2900 color receiver. The horizontal oscillator (V501) frequency is "adjusted" by a dual-diode arrangement (DD501) acting as a phase detector. The rather conventional horizontal output circuit uses a 6JE6 tube, partially controlled by high-voltage regulator Q501. A reference voltage from B-plus boost regulates Q501's conduction. The Q501 collector is tied back to the grid of the 6JE6 output tube, V502. Q501, along

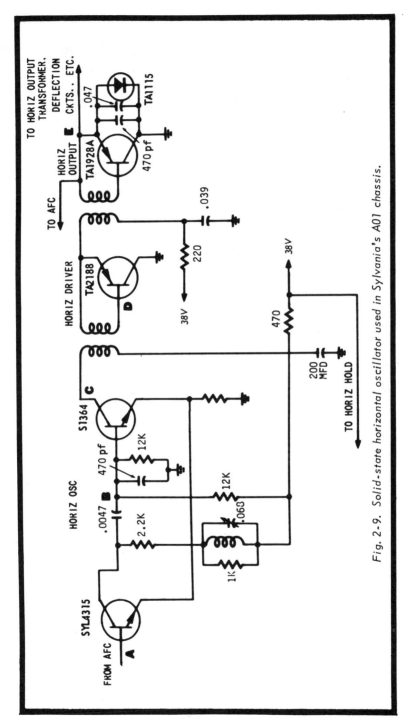

Fig. 2-9. Solid-state horizontal oscillator used in Sylvania's A01 chassis.

27

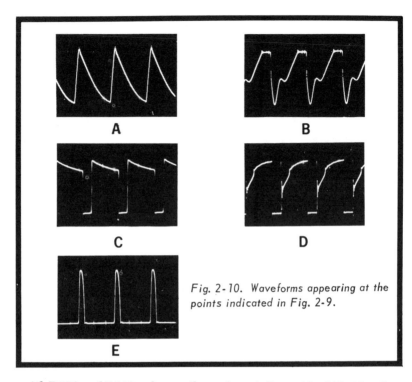

A

B

C

D

Fig. 2-10. Waveforms appearing at the points indicated in Fig. 2-9.

E

with D501 and D502, shapes the pulse at the grid of V502, thus controlling the current through V502.

Regulation problems in a circuit of this type would bring Q501 under suspicion immediately, so let's see what happens if it becomes shorted. The normal waveform at the collector of Q501 is shown in Fig. 2-12. Fig. 2-13 shows the normal waveform at the grid of V502. All waveforms in this circuit were taken with a low-capacity probe on a Hickok CRO 5000 scope. If Q501 were shorted, its collector waveform would look like Fig. 2-14. This would cause additional current flow through V502 because the grid drive would increase. Since the cathode of V502 is protected by a 3/8-amp fuse, the fuse would blow and there would be a loss of raster and high voltage. A quick check with a scope at the grid of V501A will indicate normal or abnormal operation of the horizontal oscillator. The normal waveform is shown in Fig. 2-15. The sync signal applied to the phase detector diodes is shown in Fig. 2-16. A shorted or open diode in the phase detector will cause a loss of horizontal sync and a change in the waveform at the grid of V501A.

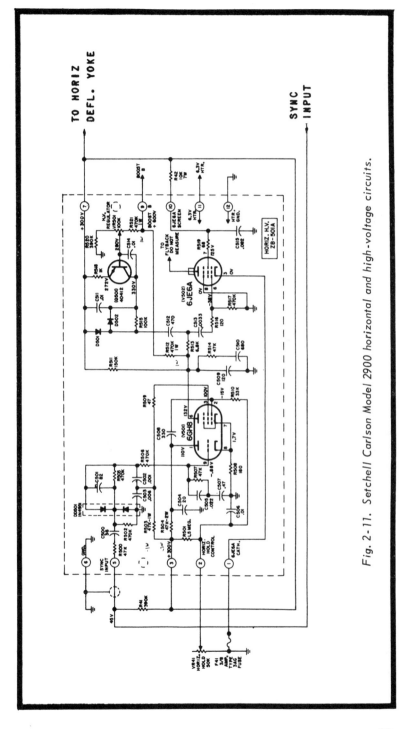

Fig. 2-11. Setchell Carlson Model 2900 horizontal and high-voltage circuits.

Fig. 2-12. Normal waveform at the Q501 collector (Fig. 2-11)

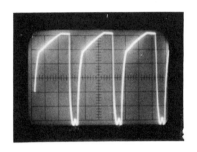

Fig. 2-13. Waveform (120VP-P) at the V502 grid (Fig. 2-11).

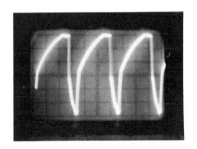

Fig. 2-14. Waveform at the Q501 (Fig. 2-11) collector with an emitter-to-base short.

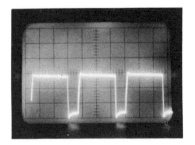

Fig. 2-15. Waveform (84VP-P) at the horizontal oscillator grid of V501 (Fig. 2-11).

LOSS OF VERTICAL SWEEP

Here's where the scope can really prove its worth. The symptom is a thin bright line across the screen. And it should be bright—the entire picture is right there! A loss of vertical sweep can be caused by almost any defective component in the vertical section. Assuming that the vertical oscillator and output tubes have been replaced, the first point to check is the grid signal at Point A of Fig. 2-17, a typical vertical circuit. Use a low-capacitance probe, and remember there is an attenuation factor of 10 to 1. The grid waveform should be a clean, positive sync pulse as shown in Fig. 2-18. If the waveform at the grid is normal, move the probe to the grid of the output tube. The waveform at Point B in Fig. 2-17 is shown in Fig. 2-19.

Normally, scope waveform analysis will disclose a loss of signal at some point in this stage which results in the loss of vertical sweep. If you are working with transistorized circuits, check the drive to the output transistor first. If there is no drive on the base, take voltage and resistance measurements in the oscillator stage. A normal drive signal and no vertical sweep means a defective part in the output section; and don't overlook the yoke or capacitors between the coils.

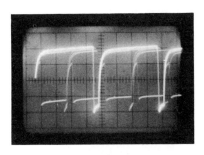

Fig. 2-16. Sync signal applied to phase detector diodes DD501 in Fig. 2-11.

Another vertical circuit is shown in Fig. 2-21. In this circuit the sync input pulse is fed to the cathode of V601A (pin 1) through a .0047-mfd capacitor. The normal sync waveform at this point is shown in Fig. 2-16. The waveform at the grid (pin 9) of V601 is shown in Fig. 2-22. There are only a few components which affect the signal at the input of V601A. Any of them can cause vertical sync problems or even a loss of vertical sweep. So the quickest check for vertical sync trouble in a circuit of this type is to check the waveforms at the grid

31

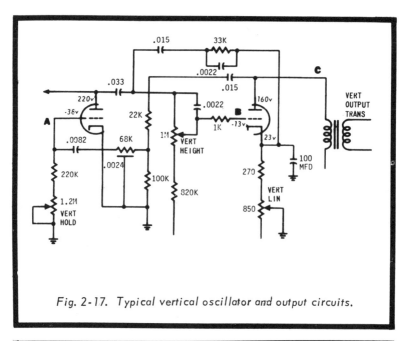

Fig. 2-17. Typical vertical oscillator and output circuits.

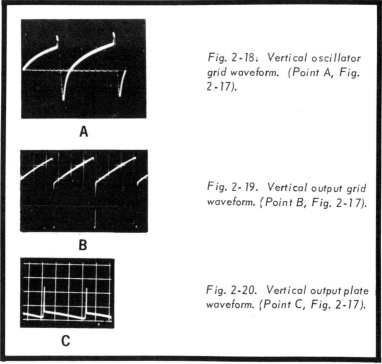

A

Fig. 2-18. Vertical oscillator grid waveform. (Point A, Fig. 2-17).

B

Fig. 2-19. Vertical output grid waveform. (Point B, Fig. 2-17).

C

Fig. 2-20. Vertical output plate waveform. (Point C, Fig. 2-17).

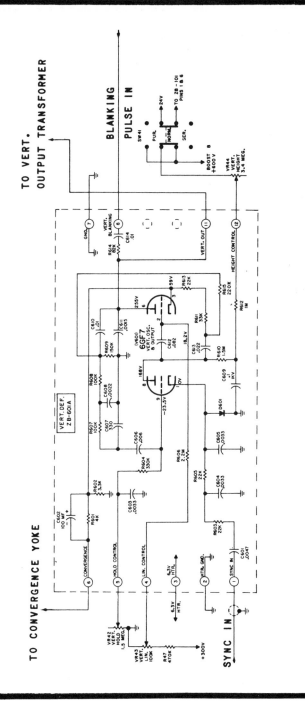

Fig. 2-21. Setchell Carlson vertical oscillator and output stage.

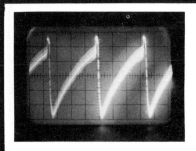

Fig. 2-22. Normal waveform at the oscillator grid (pin 9, V601) in Fig. 2-21.

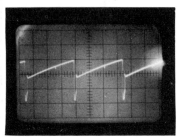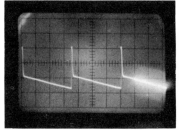

Fig. 2-23. Normal waveform (A) at the vertical output grid (pin 2, V601) and (B) plate (pin 6) in Fig. 2-21.

and plate of the vertical oscillator. Then check the grid and plate waveforms of the output tube section. Normal waveforms at V601 (pins 2 and 6) are shown in Figs. 2-23A and B.

"MOVING" PICTURES-SYNC TROUBLES

This kind of trouble is usually described by the customer as a "moving" picture; "it rolls," or in other words, it won't hold still. The picture may move vertically, horizontally, or both. The defect is likely in the sync stage and the best way to check it is with a scope.

A partial TV schematic showing a sync separator is shown in Fig. 2-24. Connect your scope to the grid of the sync separator (Point A). Be sure to use your low-capacitance probe. The waveform at the grid should look similar to that of Fig. 2-25. If everything seems normal at that point, move your probe to the plate (Point B). You should see the waveform shown in Fig. 2-26. If everything is normal, you can start looking at the horizontal or vertical sweep stages. As

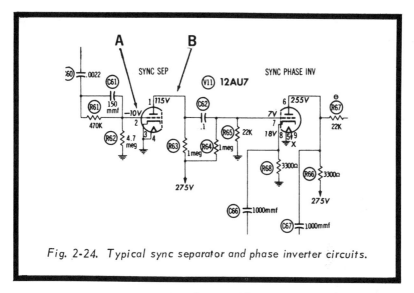

Fig. 2-24. Typical sync separator and phase inverter circuits.

before, you are narrowing the trouble to a particular stage.

The waveforms and the operation of the sync stages all are dependent on the AFC circuits. The horizontal and vertical oscillators depend on the fact that frequency can be varied by changing the bias on the oscillator control element, or in other word, its grid. Though circuits—and even principles —vary, the method of changing the bias with frequency is to combine the pulses from the sync separator with the pulses fed back from the output of the horizontal oscillator (or the horizontal output tube). The circuit is usually arranged so that if the oscillator is running on frequency, the pulses arrive so that one is at its peak as the other is about half way up its rising slope. The slowing down or speeding up of one

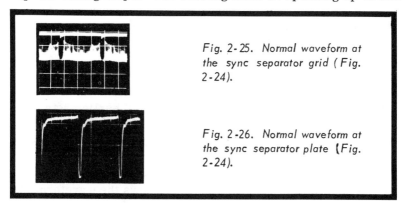

Fig. 2-25. Normal waveform at the sync separator grid (Fig. 2-24).

Fig. 2-26. Normal waveform at the sync separator plate (Fig. 2-24).

wave with respect to the other causes the pulse to "slide up or down" the other wave. If the slide is upward, the sum voltage increases; if downward, it decreases. The resulting voltage is applied to the control electrode and increases the frequency of the oscillator if it has been running slow or decreases if it has been running fast.

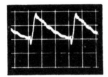

Fig. 2-27. Normal waveform appearing at the cathode (pin 3) of the synchroguide circuit in Fig. 2-5.

The Synchroguide's frequency control is the first section of the double triode in Fig. 2-5. A variation in frequency between the pulses from the sync output and the horizontal oscillator varies the grid bias on the control tube, and, therefore, its cathode current. Fig. 2-27 indicates the normal waveform at the cathode (pin 3).

The schematic diagram in Fig. 2-28 shows the video amplifier unit ZB-201B in a Setchell Carlson color receiver. This unit also contains the transistorized sync circuits. In this unit, the video information is fed from the video IF circuit to the contrast control. From there the video goes to the first video amplifier Q201 and to the base of Q203. Q203 and Q204 are connected as a Darlington pair to form the first chroma amplifier and sync amplifier. Diode D201 works with Q205 to function as a sync leveler before the sync signal goes to the sync separator, Q206. We can use our scope to check this circuit, and should see the sync waveform shown in Fig. 2-16 at the output of the sync separator, Q206. A short or open in either D201 or Q205 can cause poor vertical or horizontal sync, or both.

Most of recent sets (tubes or transistor) use a solid-state double-diode AFC circuit. One such circuit is shown in Fig. 2-29. This circuit appeared in a number of earlier sets with a 6AL5 instead of the two solid-state diodes. The principle is the same: Bias to the oscillator control electrode—the transistor base in this case—varies above or below normal as the oscillator runs slower or faster, driving the circuit back to the correct frequency. Fig. 2-30 shows the waveform at the sync input of the AFC circuit in the Sylvania A01 chassis. This is the point where the signal from the AFC circuit and the fed-back signal from the horizontal oscillator combine.

To find our trouble faster, we have taken some pretty big

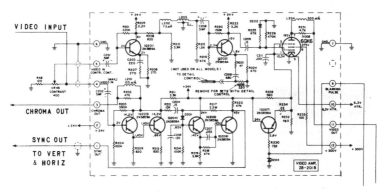

Fig. 2-28. Video amplifier circuitry used in a Setchell Carlson color receiver.

steps, in some cases jumping from one grid forward to the next; in others going back from one plate to the one before it. If our signal goes haywire between any two of these points, of course, the next thing is to check the points between; the plate

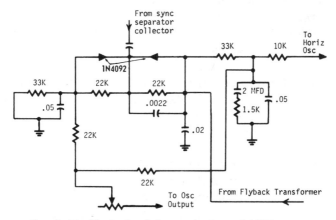

Fig. 2-29. Typical solid-state horizontal AFC circuit.

of the tube whose grid waveform we have checked; the signal on the other side of a coupling capacitor; and other points where the manual or schematic shows the correct waveform.

37

Suppose we have a problem of no video. The sound may be normal and still you have no picture. If the sound is normal and taken from the video detector, then the trouble has to be between there and the pix tube. To locate the problem quickly, connect your scope through a low-capacitance probe to the input of the picture tube. The waveform should be similar to

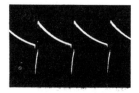

Fig. 2-30. Waveform taken at the AFC sync input in a Sylvania A01 chassis.

that of Fig. 2-31. If the waveform is normal, check the pix tube socket for poor connections.

If the problem is no video or sound, first check the low-voltage power supply. If that's OK, and you are working on a chassis where the sound is taken from the video detector, connect your scope to the output of the video detector; use the low-capacitance probe to prevent distortion of the video waveform. If the signal is normal at the video detector but not at the pix tube input, get out your multimeter and check resistances and voltages. With just a few simple checks your scope has isolated the problem to one particular section.

If the waveform is missing also at the video detector output, you will have to change to the demodulator and check the video IF stages. A demodulated video IF signal is shown in Fig. 2-32. Somewhere along the line you will find a normal signal, assuming you have first checked the tubes and power supply voltages. Signals can be traced right back to the tuner with most scopes. Patterns at the tuner test points may vary widely depending on the type of tuner, scope, and probe. Try using the low-capacitance demodulator and the straight probes, too. We must often limit ourselves to finding out whether we have a signal or not, even though we may not be able to evaluate it. Remember, too, that your scope sweep should be set at one half the horizontal scanning frequency during video checks (7875 Hz).

You have noticed that we did not mention the AGC circuitry. The reason is that while easily recognizable AC signals are applied to the AGC input, the output should be pretty much DC, and the VTVM can give us a better idea of that than the (AC) scope. Power circuits have not been mentioned either, but you can readily check with the scope to see if there is any hum by connecting the direct probe to the B-plus line. The AC ripple should be no more than 2 or 3 volts peak-to-peak (scope sweep at 60 Hz). If the AC ripple is higher than this, you probably have leaky filter capacitors.

Fig. 2-31. Typical B & W video waveform as seen at the picture tube.

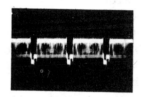

Fig. 2-32. A demodulated video waveform taken from an IF stage.

ADVANCED USES, LIMITATIONS

The scope's greatest feature is that it can locate the point of trouble in a fraction of the time other methods would take. But locating the trouble by no means exhausts the scope's usefulness. Here, we merely asked whether or not there was a perfect signal at any point. At most of those points a number of imperfect signals might be obtained, each one pointing to the nature of the trouble that produced the abnormal pattern. As pointed out earlier there are books devoted entirely to servicing with the scope. You will probably find it worthwhile to read one or more of them.

In industrial work, where pulses are frequently encountered, the scope is especially used not only to pinpoint the trouble but to give the technician an idea of what kind of trouble he has.

Industrial servicing is a specialized field, where different types of equipment may require widely different knowledge and techniques. Fortunately, most industrial equipment is simple (as compared with a television set). Manuals are rather carefully written (as a rule) with the knowledge that technicians who maintain the equipment will seldom be able to become totally familiar with it.

When we think of the scope's limitations, our first thought is of the AC scope, by far the best known to the average technician. The DC scope has its limitations, too, but you sometimes have to go a long way to run into them. Frequency response, of course, is the first limitation we think of. A "good" AC scope may be rated flat within 3 db from 6 Hz to 2.5 MHz, a DC scope from 0 (DC) to 5 MHz or even higher.

A second and important limitation of the scope is its operator. The scope display must be interpreted, and unfortunately it is almost as easy to <u>misinterpret</u> it. Further, the scope indication—unlike a pointer-type voltmeter—can be influenced; the pattern on the screen can be "improved" by misusing the controls. (The other side of the coin is that the unskilled operator may be looking at a normal circuit and get an entirely abnormal pattern by misadjusting the scope.) Scope limitations can be overcome by using more advanced models, or minimized by confining checks and measurements strictly within the limits of your own instrument. Operator limitations can be overcome by study, , familiarity with the scope—and above all, by the use of that super-servicing instrument, common sense.

CHAPTER 3

Multimeters

No doubt many readers have had some experience with the "multimeter," either VTVM or VOM. But for those who haven't, a few important words—read the instructions! On my first job, the shop owner gave me the manual and a half day to study it. Then and only then, did he let me touch the Jewell 199 volt-ohm-milliammeter-tube-capacitor tester. Today's instruments are a little less delicate; you can overload a VTVM, and the meters on most VOMs are protected with diodes. But resistors can still be burned out or overheated enough to throw the calibration off, and trying to use the ohmmeter as a voltmeter can't improve the instrument! So, it's worthwhile to study the instruction book. If you know what you're doing when you pick up a test instrument, you're much less likely to do something wrong!

VTVMs AND VOMs

The VTVM (vacuum-tube voltmeter) and the VOM (volt-ohm-milliammeter) are the same type of instrument in some respects. So we'll call them both multimeters. The main difference between them is that the VTVM is AC operated; it amplifies the voltage before measuring; its high-impedance places a much smaller "load" across the circuit under test; and it will measure higher voltage and resistance values. The VOM is basically a battery-operated device (the ohmmeter function) which is popular mainly because it is portable and easy to use. (The "M" in VTVM stands for "meter"; in VOM for "milliammeter".) A VTVM always includes an ohmmeter, though it doesn't admit it in its name; possibly it should be called VTVOM. There are a few other minor ways in which the two are not exactly alike, but the similarities are far greater than the differences.

A third instrument—the solid-state VOM—is beginning to appear. It commonly uses an FET (field-effect transistor) and combines a few of the advantages of the VTVM and VOM. One of the advantages is that is has a high input impedance; therefore, it will not affect the circuit being tested—paralleling a VTVM advantage. It also measures lower voltages than most of its rivals. The lowest range of one of the best-known is 0.5 volt—very handy for transistor work. Though it is still somewhat more expensive than the VTVM, in a few years the FETVM (field-effect transistor voltmeter) may be the most common type.

Both the VTVM and the VOM (also the FETVM) have the same type of indicator—a standard moving-coil microammeter that measures <u>current</u>. They all are able to measure voltages over a wide range by switching the meter (or the amplifying device) across a larger or smaller part of a resistor divider network. (It's a straight line of resistors, but designers like to call any combination of two or more resistors a network.) The main difference is that in the VOM the current through the line of resistors goes through the meter, while in a VTVM the voltage drop across all or part of the divider network appears at the amplifier tube grid (or transistor base) and so varies the output current which is then measured by the meter. Since the meter in the plate (or cathode) circuit of the tube measures an <u>amplified</u> current, the VTVM is more sensitive than the VOM. But extra sensitivity is used, not to give us lower-range scales, but to increase the input impedance or input resistance of the circuit.

INPUT IMPEDANCE

Contrary to what might be expected, we want to increase—not decrease—the input resistance of our meter circuit. This resistance is commonly called the input impedance. When we connect a meter to a circuit it has to draw some current from the circuit it is measuring; thus, the meter is said to "load" the circuit under test. The amount of "loading" depends on the input impedance of the meter.

As you may already know, a certain amount of current will flow through a resistor when a given voltage is applied. The rule that tells you how much current will flow in a circuit is known as Ohm's Law—probably the most important or basic rule in electronics or electricity. It says that I equals E/R. (I stands for current, E for voltage and R means resistance.) If you know any two of these values, you can find the third. For example: If a VOM has a one-milliampere meter and a one-volt internal battery, it will read full scale across a 1000-ohm resistor because R equals E/I or R is 1 volt/.001 (one-thousandth of an ampere). So when we connect the meter across a resistance in the circuit, we are actually putting another resistor across the resistor in the circuit. Consequently, part of the circuit current flows through the meter. Of course, we need only a very small amount of current to get a meter reading, so we use a very large input resistance or impedance. The higher the meter resistance, the less the current drawn by the meter, and so a smaller degree of circuit loading.

Typical resistor dividing networks for a VOM and VTVM are shown in Fig. 3-1. With the VOM switch in the 1-volt position

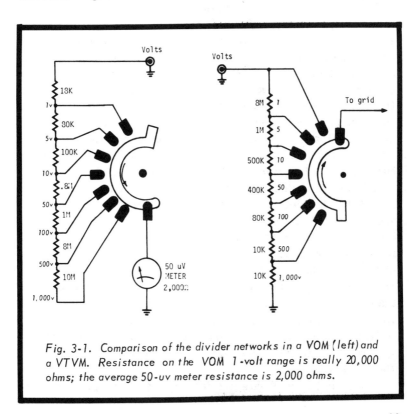

Fig. 3-1. Comparison of the divider networks in a VOM (left) and a VTVM. Resistance on the VOM 1-volt range is really 20,000 ohms; the average 50-uv meter resistance is 2,000 ohms.

(top switch terminal) we have 20,000 ohms in the circuit
(18,000 in the range multiplier and 2000 in the instrument itself). Since the meter has a 50-microampere movement, one
volt across the 20,000 ohms will cause a full-scale deflection: E equals I X R or .000050 (1 microampere is one
millionth of an ampere) times 20,000 ohms is 1 volt. With the
VOM switch in the 1000-volt (bottom switch contact) position,
we have 20 meghoms (20 million ohms) in the circuit and it
will take 1000 volts to make our 50 microammeter read full
scale.

LOW-RESISTANCE METERS vs VOLTAGE

It is established that a high input impedance is a must in a
VOM to prevent circuit loading. But a high impedance input
ensures accuracy, too. Suppose a budding new technician wants
to measure the voltages in the circuit of Fig. 3-2 and the VOM
he has available is a 1000 ohms-per-volt unit. First he measures the power supply; it reads 100 volts on the 250-volt
scale. That's OK. Now he wants to check the plate voltage
on the tube, which he expects it to be about 50 volts. But he
is surprised to find it is only 25 volts. He changes ranges to
read it on the 100-volt scale. Now the voltage has dropped to
15 volts. What has happened?

Referring to Fig. 3-2, we see that the plate resistor (500K)
and the resistance of the tube cause the supply voltage to drop
by 50 volts. This means the circuit is drawing about 1 ma of
current since I equals E (50 volts) /R (500,000 ohms) or 1
ma. When the technician connected the meter across the plate
resistor, he decreased the total resistance in the circuit to
about 167,000 ohms. This is determined by a formula for the
total resistance of two resistors in parallel: Rt equals R1 X
R2/R1 plus R2, or Rt equals 250K X 500K divided by the sum
of 250K and 500K. Rt is 166,666 ohms which rounds off to
167,000 ohms. But since the meter has a lower resistance
than the tube circuit, more current will flow through it than
through the tube circuit and cause a lower voltage reading. By
switching the meter to a lower voltage range, the situation
becomes worse because now the meter resistance is even less
than before.

Low-resistance VOMs are less costly than high-resistance

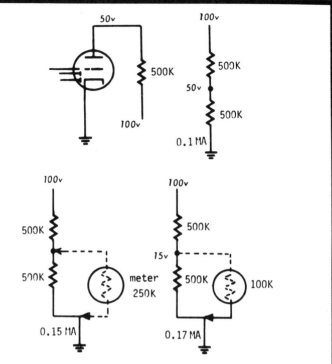

Fig. 3-2. The mystery of the vanishing voltage illustrates the effect of circuit loading caused by a VOM.

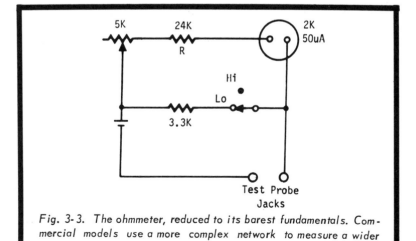

Fig. 3-3. The ohmmeter, reduced to its barest fundamentals. Commercial models use a more complex network to measure a wider range of resistances.

models and have taken a drop in popularity in recent years. The 20,000 ohm-per-volt VOM is more common today, although it is being replaced with the very high impedance FET unit. The VTVM, of course, is still popular, and it has a very high impedance even on low-voltage ranges so it will read with accuracy on all scales.

WHICH IS BEST?

At first glance, the VTVM would seem to have it all over the VOM. But let's look at it a little closer. Its most apparent advantage (high input resistance) is offset by the VOM's great portability and independence from line operation—very important in some applications. (Service technicians of a company that makes one of the best-known VTVMs are supplied with VOMs for their service work.)

The VTVM has another advantage. The current through it is limited by the tube—you can't overload it to the point where you burn it out. But most VOMs also have overload protection with a diode across the meter. That tends to equalize the meters from the burn-out point of view. So there is really little difference between the two types of meters. You may prefer one or the other for different applications. And you have to interpret the indications on one a little different than the other. Obviously, if either one would be significantly better in all respects, no one would be making the other kind now.

On the AC scales, frequency response is important for some jobs. The usual VTVM is rated accurate to within 1 db up to at least 500 kHz. The usual VOM will begin to drop off in accuracy long before that point. Some VTVMs often go up to 5 MHz before the response drops 3 db.

MILLIAMMETER OPERATION

The current-indicating function is too little used by the average technician. (That may be one of the reasons why few VTVMs have a current scale.) Current measurements are inconvenient, because to take full advantage of the current-measuring capabilities of your instrument you have to break the circuit and connect the meter in series so the circuit current flows through the meter. Since there are no protective resistors in circuit, there is also more danger of burning out the meter than when it is used as a volt or ohmmeter.

However, the voltmeter can be used to measure current in many circuits. For example, a voltmeter connected across the plate resistor in Fig. 3-2 shows 50 volts. And 50 volts across 500,000 ohms means that 0.1 ma is flowing through it, a quantity that may be difficult to read on the scales of some VOMs. But there are definitely times when it is worthwhile to go to the inconvenience of measuring the current. For example, the quickest and best way to find out if a television horizontal output circuit is operating normally is to find out how much current is flowing in the cathode circuit. (This application is covered later in this section.)

Some commercial instrument (milliammeters with tube adapters) have been built to make it easier to take horizontal current measurements. Fig. 3-12 shows one of these, the HC-8 Pacer. It is simply a set of adapters designed to fit all current horizontal output tubes, with cords that route the cathode current through a 300 ma meter. (Some hi-fi audio equipment manufacturers provide terminals on the chassis so the output tube cathode currents can be measured and the output tubes accurately balanced against each other.)

OHMMETER OPERATION

We have seen that we can measure voltage on a microammeter simply by putting an known voltage across a resistor and measuring the current through it. If we know the value of the resistor in ohms, we can use Ohm's Law (IR equals E) to determine the voltage. It is also true that if we know the voltage and current, we can find the value of the resistor—that's the principle of the ohmmeter. Now let's see how it works.

An ohmmeter is simply a voltmeter with a built-in battery, a set of resistors selected so that the meter can be made to read full scale on each range with the test prods shorted, and a meter calibrated in ohms instead of volts. Look at Fig. 3-3. Here we have a 1.5-volt battery with about 30,000 ohms in series with it. The meter will read full scale with the terminals shorted. This is 1.5 volts, actually, but we will call it zero ohms.

Now, if we attach test probes to the meter jacks, short

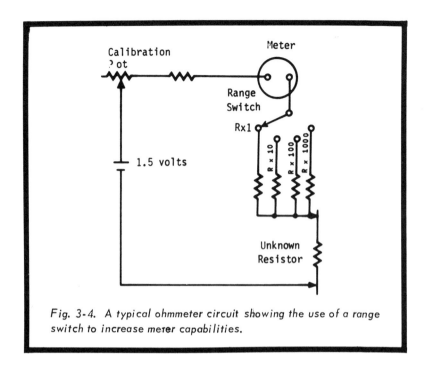

Fig. 3-4. A typical ohmmeter circuit showing the use of a range switch to increase meter capabilities.

them together, and adjust the 5,000-ohm pot so the meter reads zero ohms, we know we have about 30,000 ohms in the circuit. We know this because to draw 50 microamperes (full scale) with a 1.5-volt battery we need 30,000 ohms of resistance (R equals 1.5/.000050). Separate the test probes and the meter falls to zero. Now, if we put the probes across a 30,000-ohm resistor the indicator will rise to exactly half scale because the meter resistance and the resistor we are measuring are the same value and the current divides in half. If we were calibrating the meter, we could put a 30 at that point. This means that the meter is reading 30,000 ohms or 3 megohms, depending on the resistance of R as we switch the ohmmeter from one range to another. Notice that the scale is not linear. We used up half of it to get to 30,000 ohms; the other half would read out to 5 meghohms or so.

As we see in Fig. 3-4, one scale on the ohmmeter can be used to read any resistance, depending on the value of the multiplying resistors connected to the meter circuit by the range switch. In the R x 1 position, the meter is read directly in ohms. If we want to read higher values, we switch to the R X 10 position and now the meter reading is multiplied by 10. The R X 100 range requires that the meter reading by multiplied by 100. (See the OHMS scale in Fig. 3-5.) An actual commercial ohmmeter may be a little more complex. The multiplier resistors for the various scales may be wired in series, which saves resistors but makes the circuit harder to understand at a glance.

The zero-set pot is an ingenious way of compensating for the fact that the battery voltage, which must be exact for accurate measurement, does not remain exact in real life. Not only does the battery's voltage drop, but its own internal resistance (which is part of the resistance in the circuit) increases with age. The zero-set potentiometer reduces the total resistance in the circuit so that the meter can be made to read full scale—just as if a new battery were in place—each time the meter is used.

The ohmmeter in a VTVM is a bit simpler. See Fig. 3-6. Any one range consists of a resistor in series with a battery, usually one dry cell, and all range resistors are connected in series with a switch to select the range. Now, if a resistor is connected between the two probes, the meter will read according to the parallel resistance ratio of the two resistors. If the value of the unknown resistor is high compared with that of the one in the meter, practically all the voltage will appear across it and the meter will read near full scale. If the resistance is small compared with that of the resistor in the meter, the larger voltage drop will occur across the meter resistor and the reading drops toward zero.

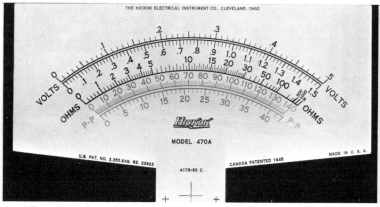

Fig. 3-5. A scale center of 10 is common on many ohmmeters.

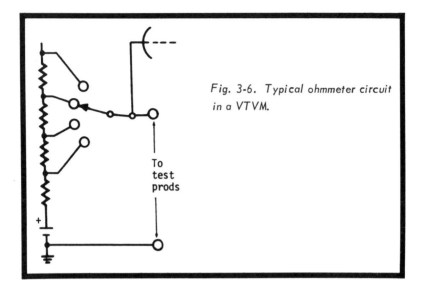

Fig. 3-6. Typical ohmmeter circuit in a VTVM.

To
test
prods

Notice that a VTVM ohmmeter function works in the opposite direction to the one in a VOM: high ohms is full-scale and zero is indicated when there is no current flowing through the meter. The VTVM ohmmeter has two adjustments—one to bias the circuitry so the meter reads full scale with the probes

Fig. 3-7. VTVMs are made in field service and bench types. Bench units feature horizontal styling and have larger meters, 6-inch in this case. This instrument is mounted so it can be tipped to any angle.

50

shorted and one sets the meter to zero with them open. So much for how an ohmmeter works. What it can do is even more important. It is one of the service technician's most important tools as we will see.

USING THE MULTIMETER

The multimeter can be used to make voltage, resistance, and current measurements in almost any type of circuit, as-

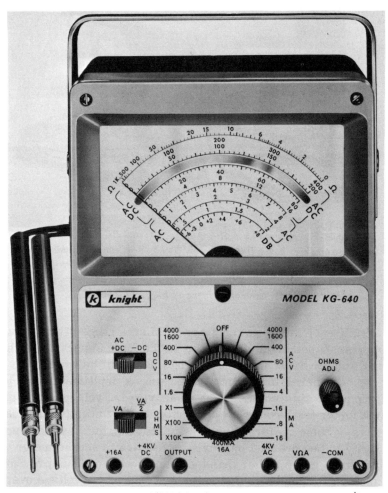

Fig. 3-8. A high-class VOM like this may cost more than an ordinary VTVM. This model features voltage ranges up to 4,000 volts (and down to 0.8 volt DC).

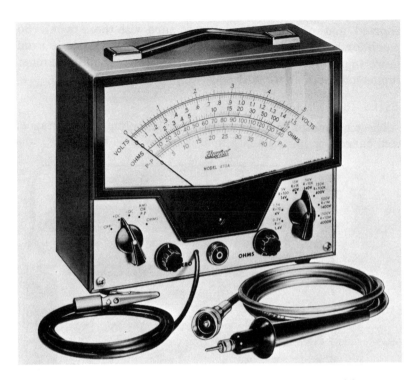

Fig. 3-9. In this VTVM all voltages, AC and DC, are read from the same two basic linear scales. It has 8 AC and DC voltage ranges, from 0.5 volt to 1,500 volts full scale; peak-to-peak ranges from 1.4 to 1,400 volts. Resistance can be measured to 1,000 megohms. Input impedance is high—17.7 megohms.

suming such measurements are within the range of the instruments. Another factor, too, is the input impedance of the multimeter itself and its affect on the circuit being tested.

Some general precautions on using a multimeter may be helpful at this point. When measuring DC voltage, be sure the meter test probes are correctly placed—negative and positive. Some meters have a switch to allow the test-lead polarity to be reversed internally. Be sure to set the meter to a voltage range higher than the supply voltage. This prevents accidental damage to the meter movement by a voltage overload. The meter can be switched to lower DC ranges as necessary once you have safely checked it on the high range. DC current measurements also require correct test lead polarity. A reading which deflects the needle downward means the meter is connected backwards. Again, be sure the meter is set to the high current range to start with, since an overload can damage the meter. The following examples describe some of the techniques of using a multimeter in various circuits.

A multimeter can be used to check oscillators, audio amplifiers, pulse amplifiers, detector circuits, transistors, diodes, capacitors, coils, resistors, and for hundreds of other uses numerous enough to fill an entire volume. However, the use of the multimeter (VOM, VTVM, FETVOM) in these circuits should give you a good idea of the multimeter's capabilities.

Oscillators are normally the most critical circuits in a two-way radio, receiver, or TV because they are designed to operate at a specific frequency with specified components. This means that any change in component values can change oscillator operation. For this reason, the test meter must not significantly affect the circuit when it is connected for voltage readings. Oscillators normally have a negative voltage on the tube grid and measurements are made with respect to the cathode, which is grounded in many cases. This means that the positive lead must be connected to ground and the neg · ative lead to the grid, or you can use the reverse polarity switch if your meter has one.

Resistance measurements in any circuit should be made with the power off, and when checking a resistor or capacitor (for leakage) one lead should be unsoldered from the circuit. Always choose a resistance range which will place the meter reading near center scale for the best accuracy. Be sure to first "zero" the meter on the range you are using. With the meter leads separated and nothing connected, the meter OHMS ZERO control is adjusted to give zero ohms. Then, short the test leads together and set the OHMS ADJUST for a full-scale reading. Now you are ready to make resistance measurements.

Audio Amplifiers

Audio amplifiers are classified into several categories: Class A and Class B being more common. Class A audio amplifiers are usually single-stage circuits and are used in many TV, radio, and hi-fi units. In a Class A amplifier the multimeter can be used to check voltages and resistance. An audio amp-

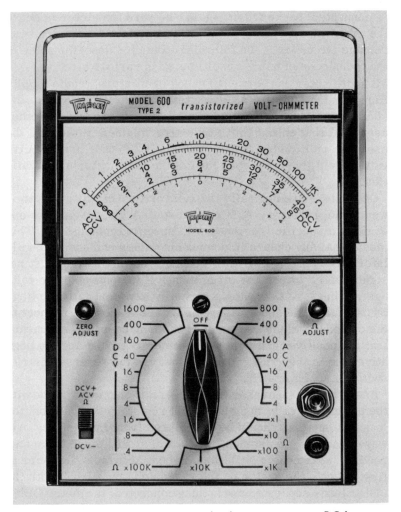

Fig. 3-10. This transistor-type volt-ohmmeter measures DC from 0.4 to 1,600 volts, AC from 4 to 800 volts. DC input impedance is 11 megohms, except on the 0.4 and 0.8 -volt ranges; AC impedance is 0.75 megohm.

lifier usually has one of three common ailments: dead, weak, or distorted, and voltage readings at various schematic test points and component resistance measurements can help to isolate the problem. However, these tests should follow a preliminary check with an audio signal generator. Speakers can be checked on a low-resistance scale with the meter probes connected to the voice coil leads. A good speaker will "click" as the probes are applied and the meter will show several ohms resistance if the scale is low enough.

Class B amplifiers are operated in pushpull—two tubes or transistors connected to add their respective power capacities. In this type of amplifier, one tube or transistor can become defective and the other will carry the load. Voltage checks of each stage will reveal the defective unit. Again, resistance checks used to follow up voltage tests can help isolate a defective component. Be sure power is turned off before resistance readings are made.

Horizontal Output

Pulse amplifier voltages, such as those associated with the horizontal output tube in a TV set, cannot be checked with a conventional multimeter. Such a stage can be checked, though, by measuring the current through the tube. In fact, this is the normal method for testing and adjusting this stage. In many color receivers the horizontal output cathode lead is brought out to a point where a milliammeter can be easily connected. With the TV turned off, the cathode lead is disconnected from the chassis and connected to the positive meter probe. The negative probe goes to ground. Set the meter for a reading of 500 ma and turn the TV set on. A normally-operating horizontal output tube will read less than 300 ma if the horizontal efficiency coil is properly tuned. The manufacturer's service manual will provide information on this.

Diodes

Most detectors found in TV and radio circuits today are crystal diodes. Since they require no B-plus operating voltage, there are no voltage readings to take. However, a diode can be checked for resistance. All diodes have a higher resistance in one direction than the other. Set the multimeter to a high resistance scale and place the meter probes across the diode. Notice the reading and make the same measurement with the leads reversed. A good diode will read as much as 100 times higher in one direction than the other. Detector diodes can often be tested in this manner right in the circuit.

Fig. 3-11. Lowest scale ranges on this FET volt-ohmmeter are 0.1 volt DC, 0.01 AC, with 10.6 megohms impedance.

Other Components

Using the multimeter to test various components requires that you under stand the differences between a VOM (or FET-VOM) and a VTVM. Since a VOM is battery-operated, resistors, coils, and diodes is an easy enough chore for most multimeters. The meter is simply set to read resistance and the test leads placed across the component. When it comes to capacitors and transistors, however, a different approach is necessary. A capacitor stores a charge, and unless it is a dead short a leaky capacitor can put a strain on a battery-operated VOM. Therefore, a VTVM is a better choice. A capacitor should be disconnected from the circuit at one end before testing. If a VOM is used, set it to the highest resistance range and connect the meter probes across it. The meter should first go to full scale then slowly fall back toward infinity. If the capacitor is a large electrolytic, a VTVM must be used because the battery in a VOM will not fully charge the capacitor. Another way to check a capacitor for shorts or leakage is to disconnect the ground or "cold" end and test for the presence of any DC voltage at the disconnected lead. Voltage usually means a defective component.

Fig. 3-12   This cathode-current tester is a milliammeter.

Transistors

Transistors can be checked quickly by using one of the modern in-circuit testers now available. However, if you don't have one, a VOM or VTVM can be used very effectively, too. The transistor has to be disconnected from the circuit, or at least two of the three leads anyway. The multimeter is first set to read resistance. If the transistor is an NPN type, place the ohmmeter positive lead on the base. Alternately connect the black lead to the collector and emitter leads—the meter should indicate a low resistance on both. Now put the negative ohmmeter lead on the base. Then alternately check the resistance at the emitter and collector with the positive lead. Both readings should be high. In fact, the transistor is much like a pair of diodes back-to-back. PNP transistors are checked the same way except the polarity is the opposite in each case.

CHAPTER 4

Putting Multimeters To Work

Faced with a piece of electronic apparatus that doesn't work, the skilled technician first asks "Where has the circuit failed?" Once he has pinned the trouble down to a definite location, he can usually find out what it is without wasting too much time. But when he does locate the trouble area, the piece of equipment he reaches for is almost invariably the multimeter.

There are several ways to locate the trouble spot. One or another of the methods has been favored above all others. Signal tracing was tremendously popular at one time, driving practically all other forms of locating trouble under cover. The signal tracer was a small, often hand-held radio receiver with one probe leading into its RF input and another to its audio section. The technician started at the antenna and checked for a signal. At the detector he switched to the audio probe. The spot where the signal disappeared was the point where he went to work with the multimeter. Off-the-air signals were favored for signal tracing, but a signal generator could be used where there were no local stations.

The signal generator offered another (and many believed faster) approach to finding defects. The audio output of the generator was connected across the output transformer primary. If a signal was heard from the speaker, the signal was applied to the grid of the preceding audio stage. The signal input was then moved toward the front end of the set a stage at a time, switching to the IF frequency ahead of the detector and to a broadcast frequency at the converter. (The usual shortcut was to tap the detector grid before starting, listening for sounds that would either clear the audio end or localize the trouble in it.) Again locating the trouble meant bringing in the multimeter.

A special type of troubleshooting using only the multimeter,

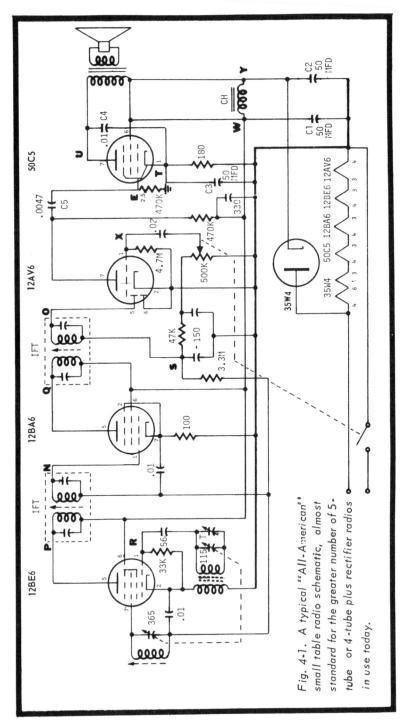

Fig. 4-1. A typical "All-American" small table radio schematic, almost standard for the greater number of 5-tube or 4-tube plus rectifier radios in use today.

and for the most part, only the ohmmeter, was popular with some technicians. It consisted of checking the resistance between a large number of points in the equipment and ground. Radio manufacturers supplied resistance tables in their data manuals. Because it used just one simple piece of equipment, it was very popular among dealers whose service departments lacked equipment. It was supposed to require a minimum of theoretical knowledge, but it had the great disadvantage of being time-consuming, and finally it disappeared .

Other fads, such as the grid-shorting technique, were prominent from time to time, but it has taken its place with the other outmoded techniques. Today the scope is the dominant troubleshooting instrument. Unlike any of the earlier instruments, the scope can show you not only whether a signal is present or not, but often just how far that signal departs from what it should be. It offers the additional advantage that it can be used with off-the-air signals or with a signal generator. But like all former trouble-locating instruments, it turns the job over to the multimeter once the approximate area of the fault has been located.

PRACTICAL SERVICING

To get the feel of using a multimeter, let's service several pieces of equipment. We will assume, of course, that the tubes have been tested and that signal tracing has isolated the problem to a certain area. We can begin with one of the most common pieces of home electronic equipment—the AC-DC radio circuit in Fig. 4-1. If all tubes light and there is no strong smell of smoke, we can start by checking the power supply voltages.

The first check should be the DC voltages. At Point Y the voltage should be about 120 and at Point W around 90. Set the meter to read DC at least 250 or 500 volts to start with. If the meter has a switch polarity, set it to positive. Connect the black lead to the ground buss line (heavy black line) and turn the set on.

Touch the red (positive) probe to Point Y and then to Point W. The reading at Point W should be less due to the voltage drop across CH. (Incidentally, CH is more likely to be a resistor than a choke.) If the voltage at Y seems high, probably not enough current is being drawn by the audio output circuit.

(We assume that you have not already found zero voltage at W; if you did, CH is open.) If the voltage at W is normal (or more likely high) the next step is to move your probe to point U, the output tube plate. High voltage here means the tube is not conducting or one of the circuit components is defective; no voltage or low voltage points to an open or near-open in the output transformer primary because the tube's B-plus voltage is supplied through the transformer. Next, try Point T, normally about 6 volts above ground. If the voltage here is too low, the tube is bad; if it's too high, the cathode resistor is open. to check the 180-ohm cathode resistor, turn the radio off. Unsolder one end of the resistor and set your ohmmeter on the low or R X 1 scale. If it reads within 10% of its value, it is still good. If the value has increased to something much higher than normal, replace it. If it is open it will, of course, read zero.

But suppose we find the voltage low at Point Y. Then the problem isn't quite so simple. The power supply may be at fault, so put in a 35W4 that is known to be good. If the voltage is still low, C1 and C2 can be checked in turn by substituting known-good capacitors. If they are leaky, bridging good capacitors across them won't help. (We could work with instruments alone and get a fair idea of the condition of C1 and C2 with the ohmmeter, but substitution is easier, quicker, and surer.

If the trouble persists, the next step is to go back to Point U, the plate of the audio output tube. Set the meter to measure DC voltage on at least the 250-volt range. If the voltage here is more than 10 or 15 volts lower than at Point Y, too much current is going through the circuit. The tube may be drawing too much or C4 may be shorted. Check the voltage at Point T. If it is low, disconnect C3 and re-check the voltage. Normal voltage now indicates that C3 was at fault and it should be replaced. If the voltage at T is high, C4 may be shorted. If you suspect that C4 is shorted, turn off the radio and disconnect it at the plate end. Set your multimeter to read resistance on the highest range. Connect the negative lead to the ground end of the capacitor and the positive lead to the disconnected end. If the capacitor is good, the meter will first swing to full scale and then slowly drop off as the capacitor charges. If the meter stays at full scale, or moves very little, the capacitor should be replaced. A shorted or leaky capacitor will read a low resistance. If C4 was not at fault, pull the 50C5 tube and check the voltage at Point E. You will almost certainly find it positive, indicating a leak from the 12AV6 plate circuit through C5. Replace C5 with a good 600-volt capacitor—one that shows no leakage with the set turned on. You should have 90 volts on the 12AV6 plate side of the capacitor and zero on the grid of the 50C5.

We can go back through the rest of the set the same way, checking plate, screen, and cathode voltages to find if there are opens between them and Point W, or between them and the negative bus (circuit ground; the heavy line in the schematic). When a voltage is the wrong value, turn the set off (or better yet, pull the plug) and use the ohmmeter. A resistance check across C4 is often quicker than disconnecting it, as is a check across the combination of C3 and the cathode resistor in parallel with it. But remember to use the ohmmeter both ways across an electrolytic; its resistance is low in the forward direction.

If the 50C5 circuit seems normal, the next point to check is the 12AV6 plate. With a 470,000-ohm plate resistor its voltage should be something over 45v DC. A low plate voltage here points to a high or open plate resistor or a shorted shunt capacitor (the 330-pfd unit). Higher-than-normal voltage would indicate a dead tube. A weak tube looks like a high resistance, while some shorted tubes show a low resistance and their plate voltages are lower than normal.

You should also have full power supply voltage at Points P and Q—the IF plates. You can use the ohmmeter here, too, with the set turned <u>off.</u> The resistance of an IF transformer primary can rise high enough to reduce reception without changing the voltage much. In checking the IF windings with the ohmmeter, resistance may vary all the way from about 5 ohms to over 20, depending on the transformer manufacturer. If you have no clue as to the proper resistance of the transformer coils, suspect any winding much higher than the others, especially if it is a plate winding. Also check the secondaries for an open (rare) between the tube grid and the grid return lead at the other end of the coil. To check IF transformers, put the multimeter on the low-resistance range (R X 1) and connect the meter leads across the primary terminals. Be sure the radio is turned off! Then check the secondary winding in the same manner. Be sure to measure grid voltages; leakage from a primary may cause a slightly positive voltage that would certainly cause trouble.

The grid return line, from Point S back to the RF or IF tube grids, should be negative and measure as a high resistance. This is the AVC (automatic volume control) line. The negative voltage here could be cancelled out by leakage through an IF transformer. (This is where your VOM can be misleading, if you don't understand it. At 20,000 ohms-per-volt on the 10-volt range, it will shunt the 3.3-megohm AVC resistor hopelessly. Even the 11 megohms of a VTVM will have some effect. I have used the 100- or 250-volt range of a VOM and watched for an indication rather than a reading.) It's fairly easy to make sure there is negative voltage in this circuit if you aren't worried about how much. The AVC signal, of course, is fed back to the RF and IF stages to automatically reduce the gain of the receiver on a stronger-than-normal signal.

Another negative point is the oscillator grid, Point R, which should be the first check point if the audio section is OK. Oscillator trouble is very common, and if this point is OK, so is the oscillator. It should run several volts negative, and it can be readily checked with a VOM. (The grid resistor across which the VOM is placed is usually lower than 50,000 ohms.) If the oscillator isn't working, you can concentrate on that stage rather than working back to it through the detector and IFs, which are less likely to give trouble. Try a new oscillator tube—one that works in another radio.

REPAIRING THE RADIO

Somewhere along the line you are going to find something abnormal—a voltage too high or too low, too much or too little resistance between certain points. Once you have located the trouble, what do you do next?

You can be sure something is not working the way it did before the equipment needed servicing. Usually a component has gone bad. Suspect tubes and transformers first, if there are any in the suspected circuit. Check tubes (and transistors if they are not an integral part of the circuitry) on a tester, or replace with known good ones. Transistors that are soldered into the circuit are usually OK if the voltages on their elements are correct. However, in critical transistor circuits, such as RF stages and oscillators, gain can be an important factor and the only way to check it is with a transistor tester. Some of the new transistor testers today will make transistor gain tests in or out of the circuit. But to be really accurate, it is best to remove the transistor. A voltmeter with a 0.5-volt range can measure a voltage of 0.1 accurately. The low scale of the $12.95 handitester, or even the 1.5-volt scale of a VTVM, may not be so useful here.

The Royal Ohmmeter

The ohmmeter is a not-so-crude capacitor tester if properly used, but disconnect one end of the capacitor from the circuit before testing it. Capacitors are checked by putting the ohmmeter range switch to its highest resistance and zeroing the meter. Then connect the meter leads to the capacitor. The meter will go to full scale then drop off toward infinity. What you are actually doing is charging the capacitor. If it's shorted, of course, it will go to zero and not show a charge. If it is open, it won't go to zero.

Electrolytic capacitors are a little harder to check as the meter leads have to be connected at the proper polarity (minus to minus and plus to plus). Also, an electrolytic can show good with the low voltage on it from the meter, but actually it can be breaking down under the higher operating voltage. Substitution is the best step when an electrolytic is suspect.

For checking capacitors in high-voltage circuits (or for other continuity and resistance checking, for that matter) you have another ohmmeter in your multitester—your voltmeter. To check a capacitor in power supply circuits, disconnect the low-voltage end of the capacitor. Then, with power on, measure the voltage between the low-voltage end and ground. Your voltmeter is now simply a high-range ohmmeter that is using the equipment's high-voltage supply instead of an internal battery. If you find any voltage at all, DC current is coming through the capacitor, possibly enough to upset the bias on the following grid. As we mentioned before, you may find that many a capacitor checks perfect on 3 volts but leaky on 250! Fig. 4-2 shows the test setup for checking a coupling capacitor using the set's B-plus voltage.

SERVICING AM-TRANSISTOR RADIOS

The multimeter has a number of other uses in servicing,

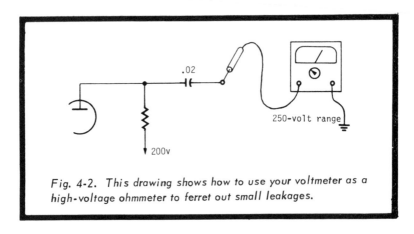

.02

250-volt range

200v

*Fig. 4-2. This drawing shows how to use your voltmeter as a
high-voltage ohmmeter to ferret out small leakages.*

whether it be radios, TVs, hi-fi or the wife's electric toaster.
The radio in Fig. 4-1 is a tube model and uses no solid-state
devices. The circuit in Fig. 4-3 is a modern solid-state AM-
FM radio and the use of a multimeter with this type receiver
requires a little more care. One important caution: In some
solid-state circuits, ground may not always be circuit ground.
Check the manufacturer's directions before connecting any test
equipment.

The B-plus voltages in solid-state units are often much lower
than in AC-DC sets. You need a VOM with a high input impedance, especially on the low-voltage scales (FET VOMs are
ideal). Defective transistors can usually be isolated by taking
voltage checks at the base, emitter, and collector. You have
to use caution when moving a probe around in these circuits
or you can accidentally short out transistors and diodes. This
would just add to your troubles in the circuit. A diode can be
checked by disconnecting one end and reading the resistance
across it. It should read low with the meter connected one
way and high with the meter leads reversed as previously indicated. If it reads low both ways, it is shorted. The ohmmeter part of your VOM is handy for checking continuity of the
printed circuit foil or "lands," too. These copper paths sometimes crack due to rough use or become shorted by sloppy
soldering during repair.

The AM-FM receiver in Fig. 4-3 has some stages common
to both AM and FM reception. A receiver problem can be
isolated to a particular area and then the multimeter can be
used to isolate a defective component. Let's assume the re-

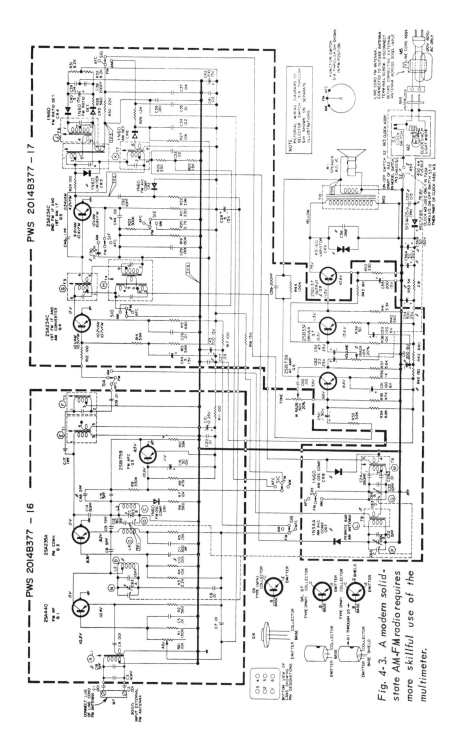

Fig. 4-3. A modern solid-state AM-FM radio requires more skillful use of the multimeter.

ceiver has no output on either AM or FM. The first thing we can check is operating B-plus voltage. Set the multimeter to read DC voltage on a range at least 150 volts. Connect the negative test lead to the chassis ground point (heavy black lead) and the positive lead to one side of the rectifier. If the B-plus voltage is normal, voltage checks in the audio circuit are the next step.

Transistor voltages should be checked with the negative meter lead attached to chassis ground. Check the output transistor, Q8, first. Measure the DC voltage at the emitter, base, and collector of each transistor. A defective transistor, resistor, or shorted capacitor will have an effect on the transistor voltages. A higher-than-normal transistor voltage means the transistor is not conducting. A low or missing voltage means an open component.

If the collector voltage is missing from Q8, check the resistance of the output transformer, T10. It could have an open primary. Another good test in the output stage is to connect the voltmeter leads across the emitter resistor of Q8 (R52) and measure the voltage as the volume control is turned full on. Observe polarity when connecting the test leads. A voltage here indicates that Q8 is conducting. No voltage can mean either R52 or C55 is defective. Voltages on transistors are measured as shown in Fig. 4-4. If a transistor is suspected as being defective, the best bet is to remove it from the circuit and test it. An ohmmeter can be used as described in Chapter 3.

Supposing our preliminary signal tracing showed the audio section and FM reception to be normal, but the receiver was dead on AM. In this case, we can isolate the problem immediately to the AM oscillator stage because the IF and audio stages are common to both AM and FM reception.

To check the oscillator comparator in this circuit, it is only necessary to check the resistance of CR8. Remember, a diode should measure a high resistance in one direction, low in the other. One end of the diode must first be unsoldered from the circuit because it is across a low-resistance winding of T9. If the problem in AM operation is noisy tuning, it could be the plates of the tuning capacitors, sections C63C and D, are shorting. A resistance test can also be made of T9. Weak reception may also be checked by measuring the

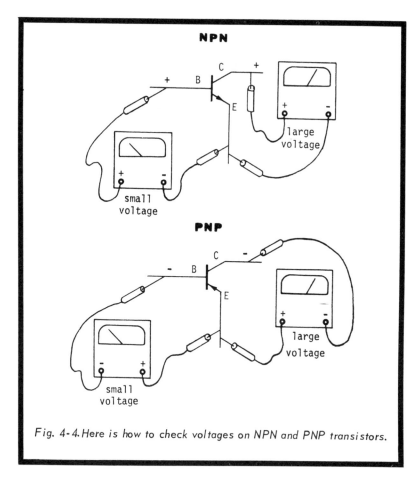

NPN

small voltage

large voltage

PNP

large voltage

small voltage

Fig. 4-4. Here is how to check voltages on NPN and PNP transistors.

resistance of T8. A problem of distortion on weak signals can often be traced to the AVC circuit. A resistance check of the AVC diode, CR7, will tell you whether it is at fault.

If the complaint is no AM reception, but the audio and FM operation check normal, you can suspect the AM detector stage. Again, the AM detector diode, CR6, can be checked by unsoldering one end and measuring its forward and backward resistance. If the receiver is dead on both AM and FM, but the audio and oscillator stages check normal, the trouble is assumed to be in the IF section since it is common to both. In this case, turn the set off, set the ohmmeter to a low-resistance scale and check the resistances of IF transformers T3 and T4. A shorted bypass capacitor in any of the IF stages can cause similar problems and these can also be checked

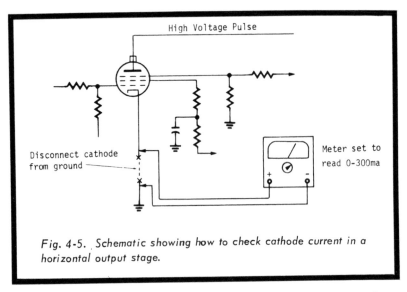

High Voltage Pulse

Disconnect cathode from ground

Meter set to read 0-300ma

Fig. 4-5. Schematic showing how to check cathode current in a horizontal output stage.

with an ohmmeter. Unsolder one end of the capacitor first and then connect the test leads across it. Be sure to set the ohmmeter to the highest range.

Another useful measurement is current flow. Many two-way radio transceivers used for police, taxi, and other industrial applications have jacks readily accessible for checking current in various stages. In other types of equipment it is often necessary to open a circuit and insert the meter. For example, the horizontal output stage in color TV receivers is "tuned" for minimum operating current by inserting a 300 ma meter in series with the cathode lead to ground. See Fig. 4-5. Some TV sets have the cathode lead conveniently brought out to a ground terminal for this purpose. To adjust the circuit, shut the TV set off and disconnect the cathode lead from ground. Set the multimeter to a current range of at least 300 ma. Connect the positive meter probe to the unconnected cathode lead and the negative lead to ground. Turn the TV set on and let it warm up. Horizontal output cathode current should be less than 300 ma; on many sets it is between 225 and 250 ma. The adjustment is made by inserting an alignment tool into the horizontal efficiency coil and tuning it for a "dip" or the lowest current reading. Some manufacturers recommend that once minimum current is reached, the slug should be backed out of the coil to increase the current by about 2 or 3 ma. Follow the manufacturer's instructions, in any case.

Many times it is necessary to troubleshoot a dead transistorized portable radio. In this example, it is best to check the total current drain of the radio because a dead short can quickly ruin the battery. The quickest way to do this is to set your meter on a high-current scale and simply connect it across the radio's on-off switch. See Fig. 4-6. The switch must be <u>off</u> so the meter is allowed to complete the circuit. If the current is low, usually a few milliamperes with the volume control at minimum, the radio is not shorted.

What do you do when you check through a whole set and find nothing wrong? All the voltages are correct, resistances right, and capacitors apparently perfect. Only trouble is, there's nothing coming out of the speaker. The trouble is almost certainly caused by something that carries signal only, without the need for supply voltages. Here is where the multimeter cannot be expected to work—signal voltages and currents are too small and frequencies too high for it. The instrument to use here is the scope, the signal tracer, the signal substitutor (signal generator) or a combination of these instruments.

Whichever one you use, the technique is to follow the <u>signal</u>

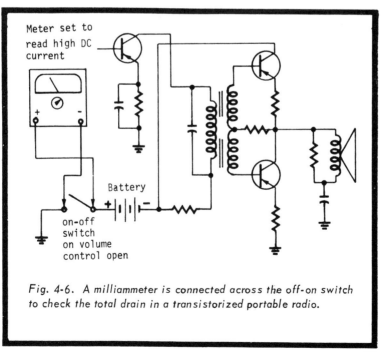

Fig. 4-6. A milliammeter is connected across the off-on switch to check the total drain in a transistorized portable radio.

through the set (forward from the speaker if you are using the generator). Your trouble is near the point where the signal drops out. Fingers, eyes, and ears are also useful service instruments. Go through the antenna circuit (if there is no signal in the first stage). Wiggle leads; resolder joints. Use all five senses. More than one antenna coil destroyed by lightning has left an unmistakeable smell while melting into a mass that defied detection by an ohmmeter. Next, suspect grid contacts at the sockets. Pull tubes out and push them back again. Continue to wiggle leads; you may improve a contact.

Watch especially for open capacitors in the signal path. For example, an open blocking capacitor (C5 in Fig. 4-1) in the audio grid circuits would stop the signal short. Or you may have a short to ground across elements that have no great voltage difference between them. A shorted trimmer capacitor in an IF grid circuit can be found by connecting one lead of the ohmmeter to the rotor and the other lead to stator. If the trimmer is shorted, it will show zero resistance as it is turned and it would ground the signal completely. A shorted trimmer across the primary coil would make a very slight difference in plate voltage but 100% difference in the operation of the set. Use tested or known-good tubes. Both have their weaknesses. But that's another story, for a later Chapter.

CHAPTER 5

Signal Generators

Most electronic equipment is built to pick up, select, amplify, shape, and otherwise modify signals. Even such far-out devices as liquid-level indicators and earthquake predictors depend on signals from some source. But in this Chapter we are going to deal with the one type of equipment that does not depend on such signals, a type that produces signals—signal generators. You might ask why signal generators are needed when we can and often do test a piece of equipment with off-the-air signals, the kind it is built to use. Well, there are at least three good reasons why it is necessary to have an artificial signal source on hand:

First, the signals we need are not always available, or when they are, such signals aren't always of the best quality. (Think of the problem you'd have with a rush alignment job on a lightning recorder or earthquake prediction apparatus.) The normal signal from a television station may be quite unreliable for testing in a fringe area, even though the signal is good enough to supply satisfactory reception to a TV set in excellent operating condition.

Second, defective equipment may not be able to pick up an ordinary signal. It is always handy to be able to blast through a weak set with a signal many times stronger than normal, or to check AGC with a more powerful signal than can be obtained from a distant station.

Third, an available signal is not always flexible enough. Not only do we have weak signals from a distant station, but in some localities the only available signal is an overly strong one from a station only a few blocks away. An artificial source can give us a signal of any desired frequency and strength at any time, and we can modify it as desired.

We may want to use other than normal received signals in

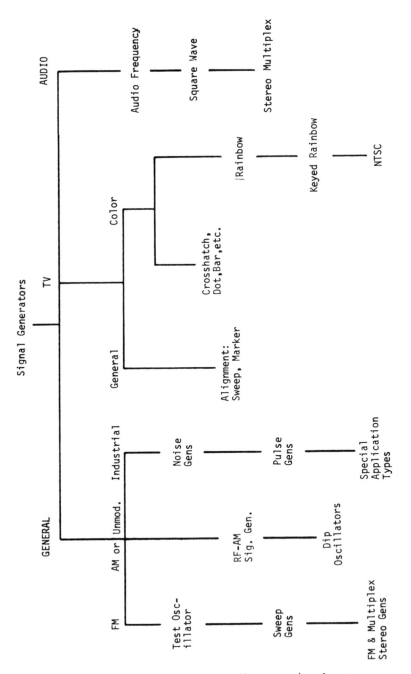

Fig. 5-1. The term "signal generator" covers a lot of territory as this chart indicates.

aligning a radio. We use an IF of 455 kHz or so—a signal we can't get off the air. And in TV work it is often more convenient to work with an audio signal (see Chapter 2) than to use the full TV transmission. So it is not surprising that signal generators are among our most popular instruments.

TYPES OF GENERATORS

There are several ways to classify signal generators. The chart in Fig. 5-1 shows some of the more important characteristics. Possibly our best approach is to start with the simplest—the bench "sig gen" to the service technician. It serves two main functions providing both RF and AF test signals. Either can be used alone, or they can be combined to put out an audio-modulated RF signal. The usual RF generator has a number of frequency ranges, which may run from about 80 kHz to 150 MHz. (Signals up to 450 MHz can be obtained by using second and third harmonics of the generator's

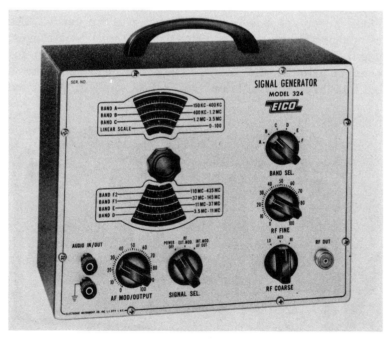

Fig. 5-2. A typical RF signal generator. It operates from 150 kHz to 145 MHz on fundamentals in six ranges and from 110 to 435 MHz on harmonics in a seventh.

fundamental signal.) The various ranges are selected with a bandswitch and the exact desired frequency with a continuous tuning control, usually a variable capacitor. A tube is normally used as the transmitter, or <u>oscillator</u>. Another oscillator tube is used to provide an audio frequency, usually at 400 Hz. The audio output can be taken directly from a jack on the panel or used to modulate the RF signal. An attenuator controls the RF output from a maximum of about 0.1 volt (on some models) down to near zero. A linear control is best; however, some units use switched-in pads. There is also a level control for the audio signal. The generator in Fig. 5-2 is typical of moderately priced instruments available now.

SPECIAL TYPES

The standard bench generator has been modified in a number of ways for special purposes. The most common is the addition of a 100-kHz crystal calibration oscillator. This provides a way of keeping the generator on frequency. The crystal produces many harmonics through the various ranges, and it is easy to detect a harmonic at 1,000 kHz (1 MHz) and even up into the VHF range. The better generators have a built-in crystal oscillator that zero-beats with the signal

Fig. 5-3. This "semi-lab" generator has a built-in crystal calibrator.

generator's own RF oscillator so the instrument can be calibrated accurately. See Fig. 5-3.

From time to time "quick-service" instruments that provide a number of spot frequencies have been introduced. These might, for example, have several frequencies available for IF and RF alignment with markers for TV and FM checks. Each frequency is selected by a pushbutton, and some models use crystals to control all or some of the frequencies. The generator pictured in Fig. 5-4 offers many pre-set frequencies for TV and radio servicing.

THE DIPPER

The grid-dip oscillator is a special type of RF generator. For some not-too-clear reason, its use has been pretty much restricted to amateur radio operators. Though the term grid-dip indicates a tube, the insturment is also available in solid-state called a "tunnel dipper." Several articles have been published on the construction of field-effect transistor dip meters, too. But regardless of the components used, the purpose is the same.

The grid-dip meter is a hand-held instrument with plug-in coils to allow operation over various frequency ranges. Figs. 5-5 and 5-6 show two popular models. It has a simple one-

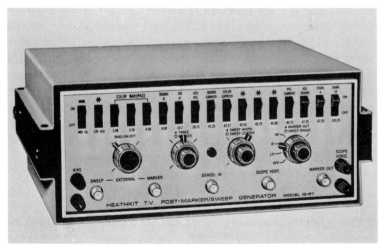

Fig. 5-4. This generator offers a number of preset frequencies for TV alignment, plus a built-in sweep generator.

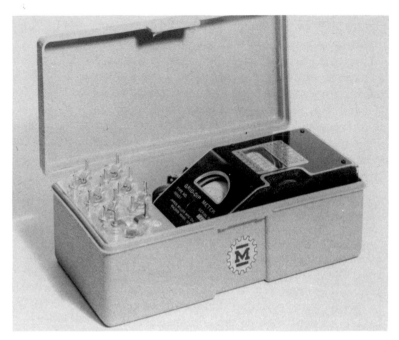

Fig. 5-5. This grid-dip oscillator operates over a range from 220 kHz to 399 MHz.

tube (or tunnel-diode) capacitor-tuned circuit, with a meter in the grid circuit or its solid-state equivalent. The plug-in coil for the appropriate frequency range is inserted into grid dipper and held close to the coil you wish to tune. The dipper is then tuned by a control until the meter on the instru-ment drops back or "dips" to some low value, indicating resonance. The resonant frequency of the coil is then read right from the frequency scale on the dipper. Although the output of the dipper is pure RF, it can be heard on the average radio as a "whooshing" sound and its presence is unmistake-able on a TV screen. So it is extremely useful as a signal injector, as well as a rough frequency calibrator.

SERVICING RADIOS

The signal generator is as useful a tool for aligning and troubleshooting radio circuits as a scope is to TV service work. The schematic diagram in Fig. 5-7 represents a typi-cal transistorized AM clock radio. Before connecting any test equipment to a radio be sure to read the manufacturer's instructions—they are important. For example, a 1-mfd isolation capacitor must be used between the ground lead of a signal generator and the radio ground. An isolation transformer may be used instead if you have one. If this set came in with a complaint of being dead, one of the first things you could check (after checking the on-off switch to be sure it works) is the B-plus voltage.

If that is normal, connect the hot lead of your audio generator to Point A, the top of the volume control. Set the generator output control so you can hear the signal. At this point it shouldn't take too much because the signal is being amplified. If there is no signal, or if it is barely

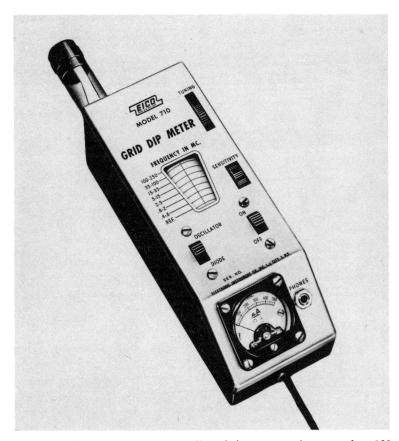

Fig. 5-6. This is an "amateur type" grid-dip meter with a range from 800 kHz to 250 MHz.

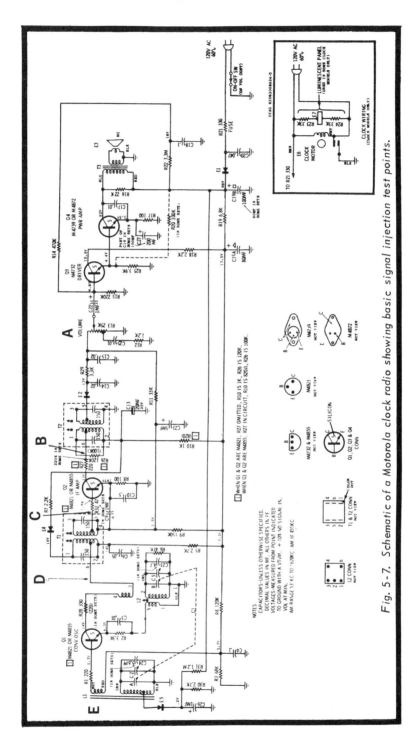

Fig. 5-7. Schematic of a Motorola clock radio showing basic signal injection test points.

audible, you should move the generator lead to the base of the next transistor (Q3) and proceed from there until a normal signal is heard. Somewhere along the line, you will find where the signal is being lost. The radio in Fig. 5-7 has only two transistors in the audio section so you should find the problem quickly. If you cannot get audio at the speaker by connecting the generator to the input of the power output transistor, pull out the multimeter and check voltages.

Assuming the audio is normal from the volume control on toward the speaker, you will probably hear some noise but no stations. This means that the front half of the radio—from the antenna to the audio detector—is at fault. Again, the quickest way to check this section is with an RF generator tuned to a broadcast frequency and coupled to the antenna input. Set the generator to provide AM modulation and place the hot lead <u>near</u> the loop antenna—do not connect it! You should be able to hear the signal in the speaker when the radio is tuned to the generator's frequency.

If you get no signal, set the modulated RF generator output to the IF frequency (455 kHz) and connect the hot lead to the output of the IF (Point B in Fig. 5-7). If you get a signal there, move the hot lead to Point C, then to Point D. You should hear the test signal at all these points. Of course, the point where the signal disappears is the place to start looking for a defective component. If you still have no signal at Point D, you have isolated the problem to the RF stage. Voltage and resistance checks will pin-point the defect. The object in using a signal generator for troubleshooting is quick isolation of a defective stage. Troubleshooting tube-type units is much the same except voltages are higher.

The same connection points are used for alignment as for troubleshooting, except that the various stages are tuned for maximum output on an audio VTVM connected across the speaker. The stages are tuned in a specific order so be sure to read the manufacturer's instructions. In the case of the radio shown in Fig. 5-7, the sequence begins with the IF transformers, T2 and T1, bottom and top cores—in that order. Then the RF section is tuned at different frequencies in the broadcast band. When using a signal generator for alignment, keep the test signal at the required level to prevent overloading the receiver. By this time you can readily appreciate the advantage of the signal generator's "controllability" feature. You have changed the frequency several times, from 400 Hz to 1500 kHz. And you have varied the gain so it won't affect the AVC and produce complications.

As indicated earlier, signal generators put out a husky signal, usually about 0.1 volt (100,000 microvolts in TV language). From that point the output can be attenuated to a level which approaches zero, at least with the better instruments. (Attenuation is normally better on the lower frequencies and when coupling to the equipment is loose.) Close-coupled to the equipment being checked, and with the attenuator in its highest position, it puts out a signal like a local broadcast station—strong and broad. Attenuated, and with the coupling loosened, you can get a very narrow, sharp signal. Loose coupling means placing the generator lead <u>near</u> enough to the receiver's antenna to just get signal—it is not a direct physical connection. Close coupling is generally a direct connection which may or may not be completed through a coupling device.

The manufacturer's service data suggests the proper methods of coupling to various parts of the set. Follow the instructions for alignment. If you need less coupling, you should find several hints in the instructions. For instance, if they say: "Use a 200-pfd capacitor," try reducing it to 50 pfd. If they say "wire loop 6 inches from the chassis," increase the distance. Some technicians use a loop from an old-time portable radio across the signal generator output and place some distance from the set being checked. When necessary, it can be moved closer, but generally you are better off with a weak, sharp signal.

Alignment

But useful as the signal generator is as a signal injector for troubleshooting, it was not designed for that purpose. It is intended for <u>aligning</u> equipment and for checking receiver sensitivity at different frequencies. Someone said that the first and most important rule in radio and TV alignment is: <u>Don't!</u> And he was right! Never start to align a TV or radio set unless you have an excellent reason to believe it needs it. The only time you really have to align a TV is when it has been innocently or deliberately sabotaged. And the story about "tightening up the little screws" is the second oldest one the radio technician knows. A radio has to be pretty old before going over the alignment will help it much. If the radio is old, a simple touch-up of the IFs may do it good. Just attach the hot lead of the sig gen to the mixer tube grid terminal. Kill the receiver oscillator by inserting a metal shim to short the plates of the oscillator section (the smaller one) of the gang capacitor. Be a little careful here—there are sets with high voltage across the capacitor. If the gang capacitor is mounted on rubber grommets, check the oscillator section stationary plates with a voltmeter.

Set the generator to the set's intermediate frequency, usually 455 kHz, and adjust the trimmers for maximum output. It is usual to start with the detector grid trimmer and work backward to the mixer plate trimmer, then go over the four trimmers a second time. A communications receiver or transistor radio may have three stages of IF; three cans instead of two. An output meter (AC voltmeter on a low range) is connected across the voice coil to indicate maximum signal during alignment.

For complete alignment—even on a small broadcast receiver—it is always a good idea to refer to the manufacturer's instructions, which are invariably included in the service manual. Fig. 5-8 illustrates the sequence alignment recommended for a typical transistor receiver. For multiband and communications receivers, the instructions are a must. I remember an old Philco broadcast and shortwave receiver that had the coils in series. It could be aligned only by starting on the highest frequency band and then working through the others in turn. (Or was it the other way around?) Starting from the wrong end made alignment impossible.

But if you have already aligned the IFs on an ordinary broadcast receiver, set the generator at about 1600 kHz, bring the hot lead close to the antenna coil, and see how close the dial pointer is to the 1600 mark when the signal is the loudest. A number of manufacturers recommend connecting a loop of several turns of wire across the signal generator output and using it to radiate signal into the set.

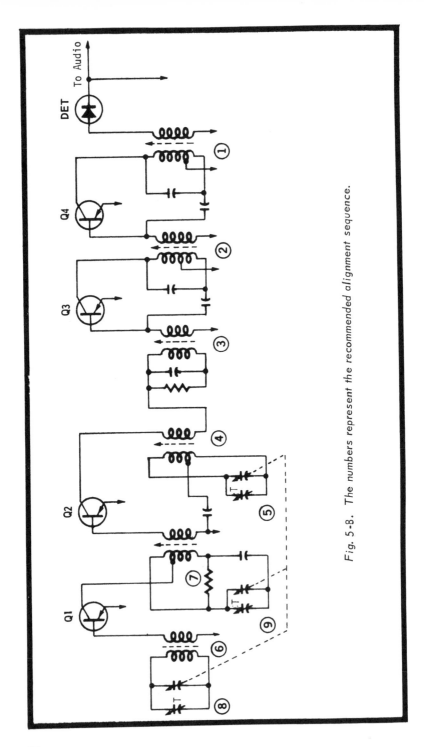

Fig. 5-8. The numbers represent the recommended alignment sequence.

If you are dealing with a communications receiver, you will find that the dial can be brought exactly to 1600 kHz with the trimmer on the oscillator section of the gang capacitor. But if you are working with a medium- or low-priced broadcast set, you have to ask yourself if it ever did track exactly. If you have reason to think it did, set the dial to 1600 and adjust the oscillator trimmer for maximum output. Then set the generator to a point below 600 kHz and adjust the low-frequency end of the broadcast band, if such an adjustment is included; a few have a trimmer capacitor (usually referred to in the instructions as a "padder") but most simply require a coil adjustment. After adjusting the low end of the broadcast band, it's a good idea to go back and readjust the trimmer at 1600 kHz; the change in the coil setting may have shifted it a little.

Manufacturer's instructions tend to vary a little from set to set. (It's always a good idea to follow them becuase the manufacturer very probably found a good reason for doing something a little different from the conventional.) On at least one small transistor set, for example, the instructions were to adjust the low-frequency end of the oscillator before setting the trimmer at the high end. With the oscillator section aligned and the receiver tracking reasonably well, all you have to do is adjust the trimmer on the other variable capacitor section (to tune the loop or antenna coil) for the loudest signal, and you have done a complete alignment job.

TV ALIGNMENT

Normally, a TV set should not need alignment unless the adjustments have been tampered with. Some circuits may need occasional "touch-ups," especially after critical parts have been replaced, but this does not mean a complete alignment. An ordinary AM-RF signal generator and an AC meter can be used to align the IF section.

The partial schematic diagarm of Fig. 5-9 shows a "stagger-tuned" video IF section where each IF transformer is tuned to a different frequency. This provides a flat frequency response over a wider bandpass. But before aligning the IF section of a TV set, read the manufacturer's instructions. Especially pay attention to bias voltage and special test jigs or pads that may have to be used to do the job right. And another thing, the traps in the circuit should be aligned first if you're doing a complete job. These traps can give you false results if they aren't set correctly to begin with.

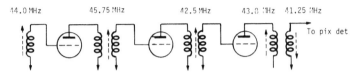

Fig. 5-9. Video IF stages are usually "stagger" tuned to provide the necessary overall bandwidth.

Trap adjustments include the 4.5-MHz trap in the output of the video IF section and the traps at the video IF input. Sound is taken from the video IF section and the 4.5 MHz trap is used after the video detector to filter out the remaining sound signal. The procedure for adjusting this trap varies slightly with each set manufacturer, but it generally requires a modulated RF signal generator with a scope. You can also use the signal from a station, but it must be reduced to a low level by putting a resistance across the antenna terminals. If a signal generator is used, set it to 4.5 MHz (modulated at 400 Hz) and connect it to the grid of the last video IF amplifier through a coupling capacitor. The scope is connected to a specified test point and the trap is tuned for minimum signal. The traps at the IF input are usually tuned with a sweep-marker generator and scope to place the desired signals at specific points on a response curve. These adjustments must follow the manufacturer's instructions, too.

Once we have the traps aligned, we can go ahead and adjust the IF transformers. The modulated RF signal generator is connected to the grid of the last video IF tube (or base of the last video IF transistor) and set to the correct frequency. Connect the AC VTVM to the detector output and set the generator output level to give you the desired reading on the AC meter according to the manufacturer's instructions. Tune the IF transformer for maximum and reduce the signal generator level to keep the meter reading where it should be. Then move the signal generator to each preceding stage and adjust each transformer in turn for maximum output at the correct frequency. Keep reducing the generator output for the proper level on the meter.

As you can see, an ordinary RF signal generator may be used for TV IF alignment, but most procedures today require the use of a sweep/marker generator and scope. These instruments are essential to the servicing of video and chroma circuits in modern color TV sets, anyway, and you can complete an alignment job in less time while observing the overall response curve of the IF as you go along.

TROUBLESHOOTING WITH SIGNAL GENERATORS

Besides being a useful instrument for alignment, the signal generator can be a handy tool for troubleshooting RF, IF, and audio circuits in radio receivers. TVs and communications equipment. The schematic diagram of Fig. 5-10 shows an AM-FM portable transistorized radio. Even though it receives both AM and FM, an AM signal generator can be used if it covers the required frequency ranges—broadcast band, 550 to 1600 kHz, and FM, 88 to 108 MHz. Most generators have an audio output signal, usually fixed at 400 or 1000 Hz, which can be used to troubleshoot audio amplifier stages.

Troubleshooting any circuit involves a bit of preliminary brainwork, as we indicated earlier. By looking at this circuit we know that if the receiver is dead on both AM and FM, the problem has to be in circuits common to both bands— either the battery, audio stages, or IF section. Obviously. the first and easiest thing to check is the battery. If that's OK, bring out the signal generator.

Set the generator to put out an audio signal and connect the test leads to the volume control, TP3. NOTE: You cannot connect the signal generator to any likely looking ground point in a transistorized unit. Check the manufacturer's directions. In this particular set the signal generator ground lead should be connected to the frame of the tuning capacitor. Then connect the hot lead to the test point. Actually, touching your finger to the volume control will tell you whether the audio stage is dead from that point, but as you get closer to the audio output stage it will take a strong audio signal from the generator to get any signal

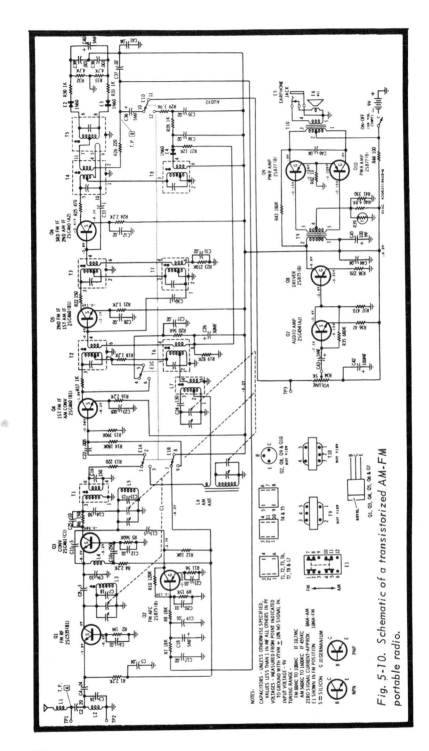

Fig. 5-10. Schematic of a transistorized AM-FM portable radio.

through it. In any case, if the audio circuit is dead at the volume control, move the audio signal to the base of driver transistor Q8. If you get a signal, you have isolated the problem to Q7 and you can start checking voltages. If you still get no signal at the base of Q8, move the audio lead to the collector. Signal here means something is wrong in Q8 or associated circuitry. If there is still no signal output, its time to check voltages and resistances in the pushpull amplifier stage.

Assuming the audio stage checked normally in the first test, we can concentrate on the IF section. For AM, T6, T7, and T8 are the IF transformers as well as the Q4, Q5, and Q6 circuits. The FM IF section consists of T2, T3, T4, and T5, and Q4, Q5, and Q6. The schematic shows the band switch in the FM position so we will feed a signal to this section and see what happens. We can use an unmodulated 10.7-MHz signal from the generator as our FM IF signal. Connect the signal generator ground to the tuning capacitor frame. Also, connect a 47-ohm resistor to the generator hot lead. Connect the hot lead (with 47-ohm resistor) to the base of Q6. If there's no signal, check the voltages in this circuit. If you have signal there, move the generator test lead to the collector of Q5, and then to the base. Somewhere along the line the signal will be absent and voltages can be checked. The same generator set to 455 kHz and modulated by 1000 Hz can be used to check the AM IF circuit. If the receiver problem is one in which only the AM or FM is dead, the best procedure is to start checking voltages in the particular RF-converter stages.

MEASURING INDUCTANCE AND CAPACITANCE

An RF signal generator can be used to determine approximate inductance and capacitance values. The procedure involves a couple of relatively simple formulas and a test set up. Although an alternative to the normal test instruments designed for measuring inductance and capacitance, the signal generator method will give a fair idea of the values you are interested in. A grid-dip meter, such as shown in Figs. 5-5 and 5-6, is a very useful tool for finding an inductance or capacitance value in a tank circuit.

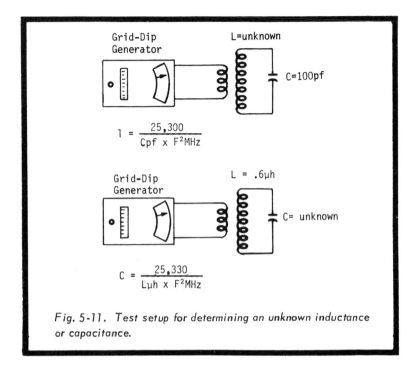

Fig. 5-11. Test setup for determining an unknown inductance or capacitance.

Referring to Fig. 5-11, we see the test set up. The grid-dip meter is coupled to the tank circuit in which we have one known and one unknown value, either L or C. There are two formulas — one for inductance (L) and one for capacitance (C) — depending on what we want to find:

$$Luhy = \frac{25,330}{Cpfd \times F^2 \ MHz}$$

or

$$Cpfd = \frac{25,330}{Luhy \times F^2 \ MHz}$$

Supposing in our tank circuit we know that the capacitor is 100 pfd. We can couple our grid-dip meter to the circuit and tune the meter until it indicates a definite "dip" in grid current, meaning the circuit is at resonance. Then, read the frequency from the dial. You should have some idea ahead of time of the approximate tank circuit frequency so you will know what range to use. If the grid-dip meter shows a current dip at 20 MHz, we can now "plug" this value into our formula along with the known value of C.

$$\text{Luhy} = \frac{25,330}{100 \times 20^2} = \frac{25,330}{100 \times 400}$$

$$= \frac{25,330}{40,000} = .63 \text{ uhy}$$

Suppose our unknown was C and our inductance was 6 uhy. Tuning our grid-dip meter we read a frequency of 12 MHz at the current dip. Again:

$$\text{Cpfd} = \frac{25,330}{.6 \times 12^2} = \frac{25,330}{.6 \times 144}$$

$$= \frac{25,330}{86.4} = 294 \text{ pfd}$$

These same values can also be found by referring to a "Reactance Chart" and inserting the two known values to find the third.

A standard LF generator will work approximately the same way; however, a sensitive DC voltmeter must be used to indicate resonance. This arrangement is shown in Fig. 5-12. The diode is used to rectify the RF signal and the .001-mfd capacitor is used as a bypass to insure DC at the meter. Set the meter to its lowest scale and the RF generator to maximum output. Tune the generator frequency to obtain maximum DC voltage on the meter; maximum voltage indicates,

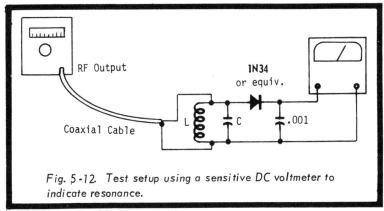

Fig. 5-12. Test setup using a sensitive DC voltmeter to indicate resonance.

resonance here, just as a current dip did in the previous example. At higher frequencies, and in some cases, depending on the generator, it may be necessary to rely on harmonics of the generator fundamental. If so, it may be difficult to get enough signal output to obtain a reading on the DC meter.

CHAPTER 6

Sweep & Color Generators

You may get away with replacing an occasional TV IF transformer and aligning it with the help of your bench signal generator. But TV signal requirements call for the use of more
than a simple AM signal generator if the receiver is to be
kept in shape. For instance, the video (pix) carrier has
to be placed not in the center of the IF bandpass but at an
exact point on one side of it, so the response falls rapidly
on the one side and rises on the other (Fig. 6-1). This gives
us the "vestigial sideband" effect which makes it possible
to save at least 25% of the bandwidth that would be required
if we used both sidebands for TV as we do for radio.

Also, the sound carrier has to be kept at a very low level.
In all present-day receivers, the sound is carried through
the IF to the detector, and if it is not kept down we get sync
buzz and sound bars in the picture. Early sets separated the
video and sound IF signals and amplified them separately,

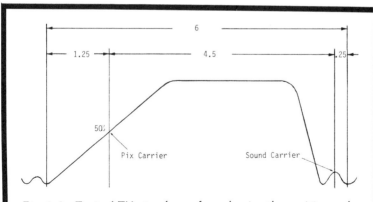

Fig. 6-1. Typical TV signal waveform showing the position and
comparative amplitudes of the sound and picture carriers. Bandwidth figures are in MHz.

improving the separation but increasing the receiver cost.)
So the TV IF response has to be fairly flat over a wide band,
then fall off within sharply defined limits at each end. You
need a sweep generator to align the IF section to meet these
conditions.

Frequency stability is one of the most important requirements of a signal generator. But, the sweep generator reverses this requirement—it's useful precisely because it's
unstable! (The earliest sweep generators were called wobulators.) Unstable may not be just the right word because the
sweep generator actually wobbles at a regularly-controlled
rate. For instance, you can set it to shift back and forth between 40 and 50 MHz at a rate of 60 times a second. Why
60 times? Because most manufacturers find it convenient
to control the "sweep" with the 60-Hz power line.) Assuming
that the sweep generator is going to be used for TV alignment,
it has to meet a few basic requirements.   It has to have a
sweep wider than the TV IF bandpass. In other words, if the
IF section is 6 MHz wide, the sweep generator should be able
to sweep a range of 10 MHz.

The value of a sweep signal depends on our most useful
instrument—the scope. Like the sweep generator, it produces a signal (internal) measurable in time. We indicated
that the sweep generator can sweep from 40 to 50 MHz (or
over any other desired band in its range) at a rate of 60 times
a second. The horizontal sweep of the scope is set to sweep
at the same rate.   The result is that the height of the spot
on the scope at the beginning (left end) of the trace shows
the strength of the signal being measured at 40 MHz; the
middle of the trace the strength at 45 MHz; and the right
end its strength at 50 MHz. By combining the two instruments we take a signal that varies with the time and spread
it out to vary with space, giving us a display we can read in
frequency.

The trace on the scope in Fig. 6-2 shows how useful that
can be. If we feed a sweep signal to the input end of the TV
IF strip and connect a scope across its output we get a curve
resembling that in Fig. 6-1. We can see where the video
carrier is, whether the IF amplifier has any undesired peaks
or dips in a band that should be flat, and that the sound
carrier is placed where it should be without being lost in a

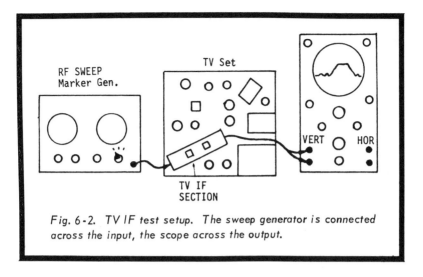

Fig. 6-2. TV IF test setup. The sweep generator is connected across the input, the scope across the output.

trap. But to be sure the signal curve is correct, we need one more thing—another signal generator.

THE MARKER GENERATOR

We have seen that we can trace a curve representing a band of frequencies on the scope. But we can't tell by looking at the scope just what those frequencies are. The sweep generator setting tells us that they run roughly from 40 to 50 MHz. But for checking the positions of video and sound carriers, we need something a little more precise. We need a marker generator.

The term really applies to its use rather than any especially unique characteristics as an instrument. Any really accurate signal generator can be used as a marker, and a marker generator can be (and often is) used as a variable-frequency signal generator. Many new sweep generators combine a crystal-controlled internal marker generator. These units are the best because they prevent distortion from overload when the sweep and marker signals are mixed. The marker generator is set to produce a steady signal somewhere within the range of the sweep-frequency generator. As the sweep gen's signal approaches that of the marker, the two signals heterodyne or mix to make a visible "pip" on the scope trace. For example, in Fig. 6-3, we have inserted a marker at the video carrier frequency, 45.75 MHz, and can adjust

95

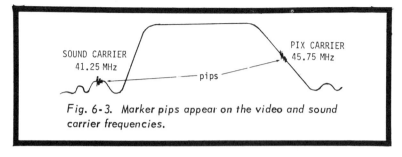

Fig. 6-3. Marker pips appear on the video and sound carrier frequencies.

our IF transformers so the marker signal strength at that point is about half way up the slope.

Don't be confused by the apparent contradiction between Fig. 6-1 and 6-3. They're both correct! When the signal reaches the receiver, the pix carrier is lower in frequency than the sound. But superheterodyne conversion reverses that. For example, the pix carrier in Fig. 6-1 may be 61.25 MHz and the sound carrier 65.75 (4.5 MHz away) in which case the oscillator in the receiver (if it's correctly tuned) is operating at 107 MHz. It beats with the pix carrier to produce 107.00 minus 61.25, or 45.75 MHz, and with the sound carrier at 107.00 minus 6575, or 41.25 MHz. The two carriers are still 4.5 MHz apart but the original lower-frequency carrier is now the higher one, and vice versa. When using the marker generator, make sure the level of the sound IF signal (41.25 MHz) is kept down where it won't put sound bars in the picture. Remember to adjust the traps before tuning the individual IFs.

USING SWEEP/MARKERS GENERATORS

Aligning a TV receiver with a sweep and marker generator is one job that you should not try without a service manual unless you are thoroughly familiar with the chassis and know the location of all adjustments. There are some general rules that apply to all sweep alignment jobs, however.

In the first place, ground everything! The technician who does a lot of alignment work keeps a large copper sheet available on which he places the TV and the test equipment needed to align it (sweep gen, marker gen, scope, VTVM, etc). Some advocate placing all test equipment on a copper-covered shelf above the bench, putting the set on another copper sheet on the bench and bonding the two together with copper braid. In some instruments the case is not connected to the circuit ground. Check to see if it is not feasible to connect them together. An isolation transformer is necessary when working with AC-DC (transformerless) receivers.

Second: make sure the set is in good condition (other than being out of alignment) before attempting alignment. Some troubles look very much like faulty alignment, yet cannot be cured by the best alignment job; other troubles make it almost impossible to align the set properly. Get everything else in order first, then—if it is still necessary—go ahead and align.

The first actual step in alignment is to disable the AGC and apply some external bias. Some sweep generators have a built-in bias supply, or you can use a bias box. (Disabling the AGC is also a good idea for IF touchups with the signal or marker generator previously mentioned.) Connect the negative terminal of the bias box to the IF AGC return (A in Fig. 6-4) and follow the instructions in the service manual as to the recommended voltage.

You can feed the signal from the marker generator into the set with the sweep signal. It is possible that the TV circuitry will degrade the marker pips, especially near the sound carrier. So some manufacturers and technicians prefer inserting markers after the signal has gone through the TV circuits, using a marker-adder. Fig. 6-5 shows a post-injection sweep and marker generator, in which the sweep signal is applied to the set, the demodulated output returned

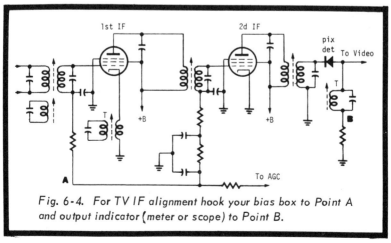

Fig. 6-4. For TV IF alignment hook your bias box to Point A and output indicator (meter or scope) to Point B.

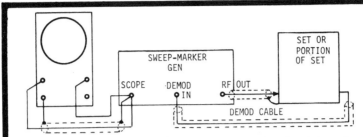

Fig. 6-5. Some sweep-marker generators send a signal through the set, then take it back and mix it with the marker signal, and then apply the signal with markers to the scope. The generator also supplies the horizontal sweep for the scope.

to the signal generator, the markers added and the complete signal forwarded to the scope.

If the markers are not post-injected—that is, if they accompany the sweep signal all the way—the TV circuit will probably absorb the marker pips, especially in the sound channel where the amplitude is kept low intentionally. A trap, if misadjusted, might be right on top of the marker. When markers are inserted with the sweep signal (pre-injected) coupling must be kept very loose—often just placing the probe near the input point is enough. This holds the markers to a sharp pip, where more coupling would tend to spread them out. It is often recommended that a capacitor of about .001 mfd be attached across the scope input terminals. This bypasses the higher frequencies that spread the pip out, leaving the center frequencies to give you a nice sharp marker. Another way to inject the sweep/marker signal is to connect the generator lead to the mixer tube shield which is pulled free from the tube socket ground clips and left on the tube loose.

With the test signals applied, the normal procedure is to set the marker generator to the video carrier first, adjust the scope pattern so you can see what you're doing, and then adjust each IF stage to the frequency specified by the manufacturer. As shown in Fig. 6-3, the video carrier is supposed to be at the 50% point on the response curve. Adjust the IF transformers a little at a time to get the proper waveform. Then set the marker to the sound carrier and make slight adjustments again to place the marker at the right point. Remember, you may not get an ideal response waveform. But if it's close to what the manufacturer recommends, be satisfied.

Some Pointers And Pitfalls

Aligning a TV IF is not the simplest job in the world. That's one reason for sticking close to the instructions in the manual. Even then, it's easy to go wrong. The job requires the use of instruments that can give misleading indications if misadjusted even slightly. If you get a display on the scope like Fig. 6-3 (the waveform representing the ideal!) the first reaction of an experienced technician is likely to be: "Something about "looks like clipping," and proceed to check the bias box, turn down the amplitude on the sweep generator and maybe on the scope, too. The ideal is hard to attain in actual practice and that long flat top looks suspiciously like the ideal. The more realistic service manual asks only that you come out with something like Fig. 6-6A. A recent Sylvania manual suggests that the technician be content with the IF curve at Fig. 6-6B.

There is no doubt that a flat top is desirable, but there are several ways to attain it in a test setup without actually having it in the receiver IF itself. One of the best ways is to use too little bias. This lets the IF tubes saturate at a low level and you get the limiting effect desirable in FM, but not in TV IF adjustment. The curve will look entirely different when the

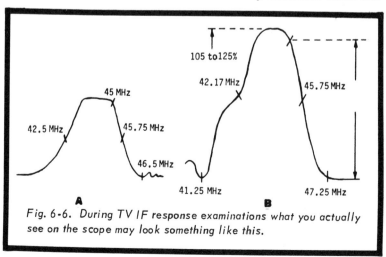

Fig. 6-6. During TV IF response examinations what you actually see on the scope may look something like this.

bias box is taken off and the AGC returned to control. Yes, you can get too much bias, too. But the trouble is easier to recognize. Too much bias will give you a white screen or a single horizontal line across the screen of the scope, with little or no indication of an IF curve at all.

A second way of getting a good "like-the-book" curve on your scope screen (but not necessarily in the IF strip) is simply to turn up the scope vertical gain control. The resultant clipping will flatten the top beautifully. Now if you narrow the sweep bandwidth the flat portion of the top can be spread out over a wider area, further improving the shape. The curve of Fig. 6-6A was probably taken with a bandwidth approaching 10 MHz. This makes the display look a little narrow but may give a better idea of what's happening in the IFs. Fig. 6-6B sacrifices beauty but moves closer to reality. The central area of the curve is allowed to go up a little above the desired amount. From the shape of the curve it is obvious that there is no clipping.

Another precaution in regard to clipping: Keep the input signal low! You can get clipping in the IF stages with normal bias if you put in enough signal. It's also a good idea to pull the horizontal output tube to prevent its harmonics from getting mixed up in the problem. If you have a series-string chassis, leave the tube in but open the cathode circuit by unsoldering it at the most convenient place.

Alignment instructions are given explicitly in step-by-step form in the service manual for each model so it would be a waste of time to try to go into more detail here. Each set has its own test points—its own arrangement of adjustments. Use the manual; you need it as much to locate the adjustments on the chassis as you do to follow the procedure.

COLOR TV TEST INSTRUMENTS

Color TV alignment calls for another "breed" of generator for checking and adjusting color rendition and a bar, dot, or cross-hatch generator for convergence. The present tendency is to combine all these into one instrument, and today it might be impossible to go out and buy only a dot generator, the one-time standard test instrument for the beginning color service technician.

Color-bar generators some in three types: rainbow, gated rainbow, and NTSC. The NTSC generator is actually a miniature color television transmitter producing colors identical to those sent out by color TV broadcast stations, with the exact phase and luminance level specified. This type of generator is normally used by laboratories or broadcast stations and may cost thousands of dollars. At least one brand, however, is sold at a price under $200 and might be the tool for the technician who wants to be able to do everything. The keyed rainbow and rainbow types will give quite satisfactory service to the technician who understands their limitations and is willing to live within them.

A color generator is really two generators in one. The actual generator which produces the color signals operates on or near the color-carrier frequency. This generator modulates an RF oscillator operating on one or more of the TV channels.

The rainbow generator contains an oscillator tuned to 3.563, 795 MHz—15,750 Hz (one scanning line) below the color-carrier frequency. This modulates the generator that produces one or more of the channel frequencies. Since its color modulator is one scanning line lower in frequency than the carrier, it loses a complete cycle for each horizontal line in the picture. That is, if it starts out in phase at the beginning of a horizontal line, it loses a complete cycle each sweep starting the next line in phase again. Since color is phase-modulated on the carrier, this gives us all the colors.

It is similar to a clock that loses one hour out of each twelve. As seen from the minute hand of a clock running on time (our scanning frequency) the hour hand takes up every position on the dial during the 12 hours: in phase at the start, 90° behind (quarter hour slow) in 3 hours; 180° (half hour slow) in 6. Nine hours after starting, we are around 270° (45 minutes) and at the end of 12 hours, the two hands are "in phase" again at 12.

The color subcarrier is phase-modulated to produce the various colors. The red signal appears at from 90° to 105° after the zero phase point indicated by the burst or timing signal; a blue signal appears at about 189° with greens appearing 90° further on. (These phase angles vary in some sets.) Thus the color generator, because of its "slow clock" effect shows one color after another as the beam moves across the screen in the horizontal trace. There is, of course, no definite dividing line between the colors—they blend into a rainbow.

The rainbow generator is a useful troubleshooter. It gives an instant and dependable signal for installations where or when signals from the TV station may be lacking or undependable; it spots faulty phase control adjustment and can be used to adjust color hold. Weak colors indicate trouble or weak tubes in the corresponding color circuitry; if one color is completely absent the technician can look for a dead tube, dead gun in the kinescope, or a complete breakdown of one of the color circuits. But the rainbow generator has its limitations. It can tell you whether a given color is present or missing, but it can't tell you exactly where it is—it can't set limits close enough to let you use it to adjust color demodulators, for example.

The keyed rainbow generator is an improved instrument. It is crystal-controlled to run exactly 15,750 Hz slower than the subcarrier signal. Another crystal-controlled circuit cuts off 12 times during each horizontal line, cutting the display into 12 evenly spaced bars with sharply defined edges. Two of these bars are lost in the sync-retrace-color-burst

Fig. 6-7. The keyed-rainbow generator produces a pattern of 10 bars, with black strips between.

part of the cycle, so what we see on the TV screen are 10 vertical color bars divided by 10 colorless bars of equal width (Fig. 6-7).

The keyed rainbow generator can be used for fairly accurate color demodulator alignment in the home without a scope. The R minus Y signal is peaked on the third bar and the B minus Ẏ on the sixth. With the red and green guns killed, there should be no difference between the brightness of the third bar and the no-color areas adjacent to it. The alignment can be carried on in the same way for the other two colors. A final check will show all bars equally bright.

The NTSC Generator

The ideal signal generator, of course, would be one that would give us exactly the same signal as a TV station transmitting bars or single colors. The NTSC color signal is a rather complicated thing, quite a bit different from the one transmitted by the rainbow generator, keyed or unkeyed. The color television signal is made up of the outputs of three camera tubes: red, green and blue. The eye is not equally sensitive to all colors and it was found that to get an image on the TV screen that would look normal in black-and-white (also formed by mixing the output of the three color signals) as well as in color, a mixture of 59% from the green camera, 30% from the red one, and 11% from the blue camera was needed to give correct balance of color, light, and shade. So each color is not transmitted in equal amounts as is the case with the rainbow generator (See Fig. 6-8). A true NTSC color generator transmits a signal identical to that from a TV station and thus makes it possible to adjust not only the demodulator phase but also the relative amplitude of the color signals. As you might suppose, this type of generator is expensive and is generally used by manufacturers, broadcast stations, and laboratories.

There are various modifications of the NTSC generator, some produce a single bar of color at a time, and at least one displays three bars. These—as well as the laboratory-type generator—can be used to check for correct color demodulation.

As with the keyed rainbow, if color is maximum at one axis, there will be a null 90° from it. Thus, with a gen-

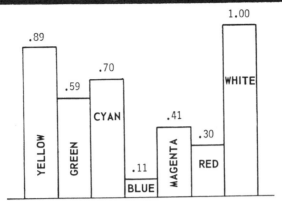

Fig. 6-8. Sketch showing the makeup of the NTSC color signal.

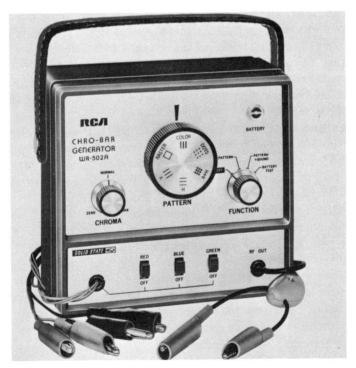

Fig. 6-9. This Chro-Bar solid-state color-bar generator contains some 20 transistors, 5 quartz crystals (controlling signals from the sound IF to the color burst), and 3 diodes. It produces a keyed rainbow pattern, plus dots, cross-hatch, horizontal and vertical bars, and even a blank raster. It is powered by a 4.2-volt mercury battery.

erator signal at the R minus Y and B minus Y axes, a scope across the B minus Y amplifier output while the generator is producing an R minus Y signal should show minimum output, and vice versa. But when the scope is across the G minus Y output the situation is a little different because the green is made up of the red and blue signals. With the generator producing a B minus Y signal, the G minus Y output should show a negative-going signal 19% of that on the B minus Y output, and with the generator producing R minus Y the G minus Y signal will be 51% of that at the R minus Y output. The color blend in relation to the brightness signal can easily be checked by attaching the scope to the Y output (in practically all cases the cathode of the color tube). The heights of the various color bars should follow Fig. 6-8.

Dots, Cross-Hatches And Special Generators

The dot generator used to be the one the color technician couldn't get along without, since convergence was the one thing that gave him more trouble than anything else in color TV. Now the dot generator usually forms part of the combination color-bar generator that makes lines, bars and cross-hatches, as well as color bars. The usual generator supplies from 12 to 15 horizontal and 8 to 10 vertical lines, These lines can be displayed separately or combined to form a cross-hatch. Figs. 6-9, and 6-10 picture two generators capable of producing many useful patterns.

Additional patterns are available from some generators: a single horizontal or vertical line, a dot, or a cross. The single dot is used for an adjustment preliminary to convergence—it is set exactly at the center of the screen and the technician can start converging without being distracted by other dots in the area. The cross is also a centering device, making it easy to center the raster accurately. Centering after convergence can throw off the adjustments already made.

A unique instrument in the TV service field is the B & K TV Analyst (See Fig. 6-11). An "everything" generator and service tool, it not only supplies color bars and the usual cross-hatch and dot patterns, but also a number of other signals (vertical output drive signal, horizontal output drive

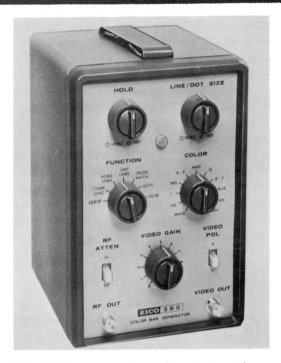

Fig. 6-10. This Eico generator produces horizontal or vertical lines, crosshatch, and dots.

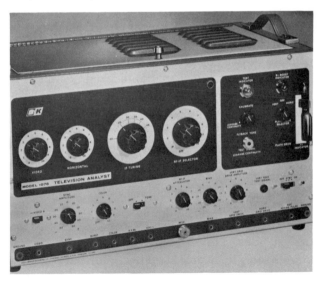

Fig. 6-11. An NTSC generator designed for the technician.

signal, 400-Hz audio note, 4.5-MHz sound channel, sync signals and other test signals). It also includes a bias supply, plus a high-level AGC pulse for testing keyed AGC systems.

Besides the color bars, the Analyst has its own flying-spot scanner and phototube making it a small TV transmitter complete with audio and video modulation. You can make your color-bar pattern by inserting a transparency made up like Fig. 6-7 into your instrument and see the number and names of the bars right on the TV screen. Or you can put in a color photographic transparency (3 x 4-inch) and check the performance of the TV set against the pictures of autumn leaves you made on your vacation trip last Fall. The scanning device has another use: You can put a set in your show window and use it to make closed-circuit TV announcements!

Another interesting generator is the RCA WR-99A (Fig. 6-12). It's a marker generator that can also be used as a re-

Fig. 6-12. Here, one generator acts as both sweep and marker, as well as sweeping the scope. A post-injection type, its operation is indicated in Fig. 6-5.

broadcast transmitter, picking up a video signal from a TV receiver and transmitting it on any VHF channel. It is also a heterodyne frequency meter. Signals of an unknown frequency from 19 to 260 MHz can be fed into it where they will beat with the internal variable-frequency oscillator. At zero-beat, the frequency of the unknown signal is read directly from the dial scale. Crystal calibrators at 1 MHz and 10 MHz, provided to calibrate the instrument itself, can be used with external equipment to produce a large number of frequencies from 1 MHz up. There is also a crystal-controlled 4.5-MHz frequency. A 600-Hz note, used primarily for sound IF and detector adjustment, may also be used to produce a bar pattern on the TV screen.

COLOR DEMODULATOR ADJUSTMENT

The color-bar generator is used to adjust the TV demodulator section for best overall color range. There are various ways this can be done. Some methods require only a color-bar generator, the color TV, and a pair of good eyes. It is not as accurate as a lab procedure, which requires a good wideband scope in addition to the previously indicated instruments.

A fairly accurate alignment of the demodulator can be made in the customer's home by connecting the color-bar generator to the VHF antenna terminals. Set the TV channel selector to an unused lower channel, one that coincides with the channels available on your color-bar generator, of course. Set the TV color hue or tint control to mid-range and adjust the generator for a 10-bar color pattern on the screen. Now, tune the burst transformer in the TV slowly until the fourth bar in from the left side becomes magenta (see Fig. 6-7). This is not an exact adjustment, but if it is properly made the color bars will change from green on the left to green on the right as the hue or tint control is rotated from one extreme to the other.

Another method of adjusting the color demodulator requires the same set up as before, except the color gun killer leads from the color generator are connected as recommended in the manufacturers instructions. Be sure the tint control on the TV is set to mid-range. Tune the color generator for a 10-bar pattern on the screen, then kill the blue and green

Fig. 6-13. Oscilloscope waveform showing adjustment of the color sync transformer for maximum amplitude of the third bar with the scope connected to the output of the R-Y amplifier (red grid of the CRT).

guns. Adjust the burst transformer until the sixth bar from the left blends in with the background. Now restore the blue gun to normal and kill the red gun so both the red and green are out. This should make the third and ninth bars the same as the background. If they aren't, adjust the CW transformer until these bars blend in. To check these adjustments, switch the green gun back to normal operation and kill the blue gun so both red and blue are out. This should cause the first and seventh bars to blend with the background. If not, go back through the burst and CW transformer adjustments.

The other method of demodulator alignment calls for an oscilloscope. The color-bar generator is connected just as it was before, with the tint or hue control set to mid-range. For the actual alignment adjustments, refer to the TV manufacturer's instructions. The method described here is a general procedure. With a 10-bar color pattern on the TV screen, connect the scope to the output of the R minus Y amplifier and adjust the color sync transformer for a maximum positive amplitude of the third bar. See Fig. 6-13. This is the R minus Y bar from the generator and it should be at maximum in the positive direction on the 6th bar. See Fig. 6-14.

COLOR RECEIVER SETUP ADJUSTMENTS

There are a number of basic setup adjustments required when a color TV set is first installed. These include the

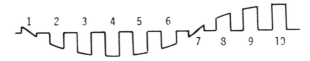

Fig. 6-14. Oscilloscope waveform showing adjustment of the CW transformer for maximum amplitude of the sixth bar with the scope connected to the output of the B-Y amplifier (blue grid of the CRT).

routine adjustment of contrast, brightness, tint or hue, color level, and focusing. Along with these are the adjustments for purity, color temperature, and convergence. Convergence requires the use of a stable color-bar generator for best results, although some technicians indicate that a set can be properly converged without one. The manufacturer's instructions normally indicate the procedure for setting contrast, brightness, etc.; and with the exception of focus, these controls are usually set by the customer to suit his viewing preference.

Purity Adjustments

Purity is adjusted with a red field on the screen. The usual procedure is to turn the blue and green gun controls to minimum. Then, loosen the picture tube yoke and pull it back until a red ball appears in the center of the screen. The purity ring magnets are adjusted to produce the clear red ball if necessary. Slide the yoke forward (toward the CRT face) until the red field completely fills the screen. You can give the purity magnets a slight touch-up if needed to properly fill the screen. Now return the blue and green screen controls to their normal positions. They will be adjusted next.

Color Temperature Controls

The color temperature controls set the emission levels of the color guns to achieve the best overall black-and-white reproduction and for proper color gun balance. There is no one special procedure for all color sets; each manufacturer knows his set best and accordingly recommends a certain procedure to follow. The procedure outlined here is general. The first step is to turn the brightness control to minimum and switch to an unused channel. If the TV set has a set-up switch, place it in the SERVICE position. This will result in a thin horizontal line across the screen.

Reduce the blue and green screen controls to minimum and set the red screen for a barely visible red line. Advance the blue and green screen controls for the same level. If one of the guns is weak and does not produce a line, increase the CRT bias until it does. Be sure all guns are at the same level. Return the SERVICE switch to normal and check the raster for a normal B/W background. If there appears to be a color tint from any one gun, reduce that gun control as necessary. If the raster background is "flaking" with colored snow or "confetti," adjust the color killer control until all traces of the snow just disappear. Now, reset the brightness to normal and check the set on a color telecast.

Convergence Adjustments

Convergence adjustments should be checked when a new color TV is installed or after major repairs. There are two "systems" to converge—static and dynamic. Static convergence brings the three electron beams into a dot pattern by careful adjustment of the red, blue, and green magnets and a lateral blue magnet. Dynamic convergence achieves proper alignment of the vertical and horizontal color beams. Before attempting convergence, make sure the horizontal and vertical linearity as well as centering adjustments are correct, as these do affect convergence.

Static Convergence

Static convergence is made with the color generator connected to the TV antenna terminals and the set tuned to an unused channel. Set the color-bar generator on the same channel and switch it to a dot pattern. Adjust the generator and TV set controls for sharp, clear dots at the center of the screen. Now, adjust the red, blue, and green magnets to produce white dots at center screen. The diagram in Fig. 6-15 shows the direction of beam movement. Careful ad-

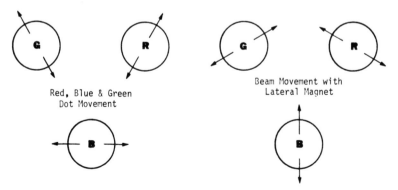

Red, Blue & Green
Dot Movement

Beam Movement with
Lateral Magnet

Fig. 6-15. Diagram of dot movement with the red, blue and green magnets, and the blue lateral magnet.

(a) Preset all H and V convergence controls to midrange.
(b) Adjust magnets to produce white dots in center of screen (static)
(c) Short out blue gun.

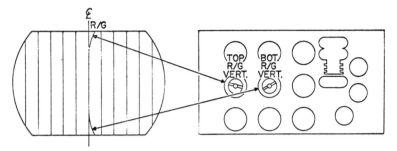

(a) Converge center bar at bottom.
(b) Converge center bar at top.
(c) Touch up both for best convergence along entire center line.

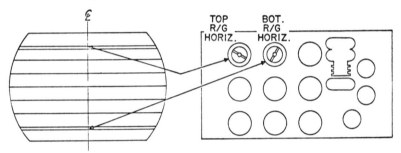

(a) Converge bottom horizontal bar at center line.
(b) Converge top horizontal bar at center line.
(c) Touch up both for best convergence of all bars at center line.
(d) Center converge (static)
(e) Remove blue gun jumper.

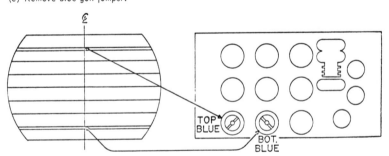

(a) Displacement of blue bar top & bottom at C/L.
(b) Equal displacement top & bottom at C/L.
(c) Adjust both for equal displacement of all bars at C/L from top to bottom.
(d) Center converge (static).
(e) Retouch both controls for best convergence along C/L.

Fig. 6-16. Diagram showing the convergence of the vertical lines and their corresponding controls. (Courtesy Setchell Carlson)

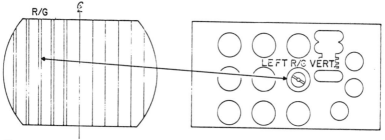

Converge vertical lines at left side of center.

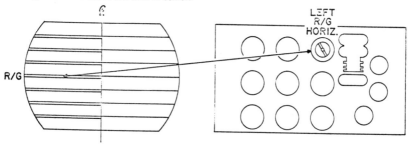

(a) Converge red and green lines at left side of center.
(b) Repeat to converge vertical lines at left side of center.
(c) Readjust to make blue line at left center a straight line and converge with red and green.

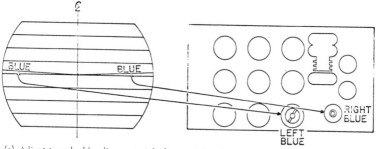

(a) Adjust to make blue line a straight line at right of center.
(b) Adjust to make blue line a straight line at left of center.

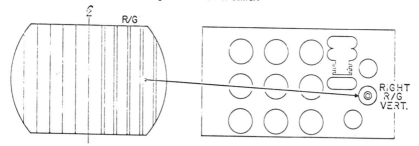

Converge vertical lines on right side.

Fig. 6-17. Continued on next page.

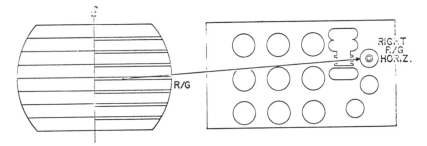

(c) Converge horizontal red & green lines on right side.

(b) Readjust to make blue line at right center converge with red and green.

(c) Retouch for convergence of vertical lines on right side.

Fig. 6-17. Diagram showing the convergence of the horizontal lines and their corresponding controls. (Courtesy Setchell Carlson)

justment of the gun magnets and the lateral magnet should produce enough travel, they can be taken out and reversed in many sets.

Dynamic Convergence

The equipment setup for dynamic convergence is the same as static, except that now we are concerned with the vertical and horizontal line convergence. Some manufacturers suggest that this convergence be done first on vertical lines, then horizontal. Others recommend using a cross-hatch pattern. In both cases, vertical and horizontal convergence adjustments are completed in sequence and then touched up at various points in the procedure because various controls interact. The diagram in Figs. 6-16 and 6-17 show typical convergence adjustments and their effect.

TROUBLESHOOTING

Color generators and sweep equipment are as basic to troubleshooting a color TV set as a wrench to an auto mechanic. There are many sharp technicians who will always find faster and better ways to troubleshoot any circuit and so the procedures set down here may not be the only ones.

A color TV receiver has many circuits similar to those of a B/W unit—the tuner, IF, and sound circuits for example. But there are circuits used only in color reception, and here good, effective troubleshooting procedures are

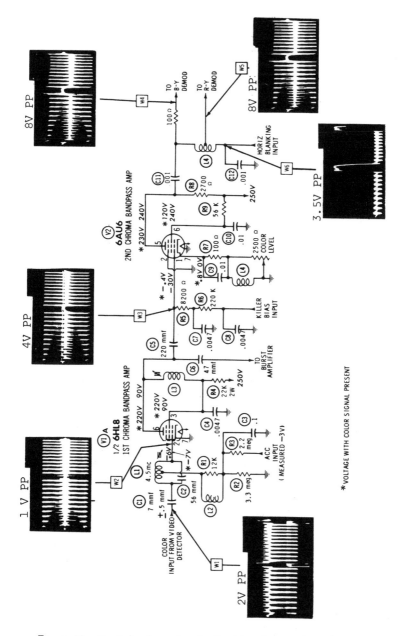

Fig. 6-18. Partial schematic of a Zenith color receiver showing color waveforms at various points in the circuit (Courtesy Sencore).

115

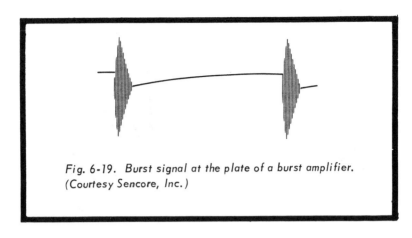

Fig. 6-19. Burst signal at the plate of a burst amplifier. (Courtesy Sencore, Inc.)

necessary. Before any test equipment is used, go through a check of the receiver controls as you would for a B/W set. Check for a proper B/W picture on all channels; check the sound, color killer controls, gun controls, linearity, brightness, etc. Then if necessary, start your troubleshooting.

Let's check several of those "peculiar" color circuits, beginning with the bandpass amplifier shown in Fig. 6-18. A color-bar generator is connected to the TV antenna terminals and set to produce bars. Then using a wideband scope with a low-capacity probe, we can quickly check the waveforms at various points in the circuit. If a signal is missing or distorted at any particular point, it usually means a defective component or misalignment. In any case, with a color signal and a scope to trace it with you can quickly isolate the problem to one area, which can then be checked with a multi-meter. At the output of the first bandpass amplifier (Fig. 6-18) the signal goes to the burst amplifier. The normal signal at the burst plate amplifier is shown in Fig. 6-19. Burst signal is present only when color is being received.

Problems in the video IF section (Fig. 6-20) can be isolated by injecting a signal from a sweep generator and connecting a wideband scope to the video detector output (terminal 12). The manufacturer's service instructions should be followed for the recommended test equipment connections. The sweep generator signal is applied to the VHF tuner mixer grid. (Don't forget to get the TV and generator to an unused channel.) The scope should show a response curve as in Fig. 6-21.

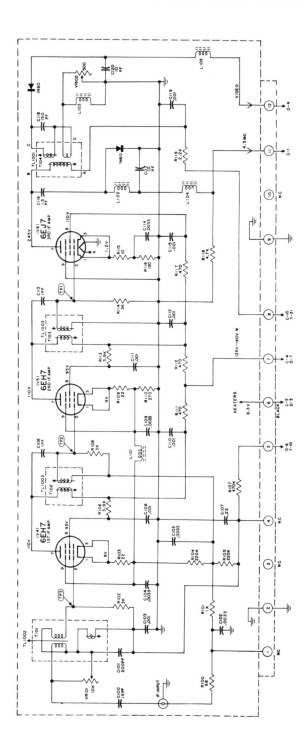

Fig. 6-20. Video IF circuit from the Setchell Carlson U800 chassis series. (Courtesy Setchell Carlson)

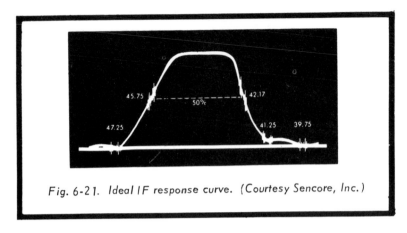

Fig. 6-21. Ideal IF response curve. (Courtesy Sencore, Inc.)

The proper marker points are also shown. If a waveform similar to this shows distortion or is missing, the signal generator input can be moved to individual IF stages.

Assuming the signal is distorted or missing at the video output, we can reconnect the sweep generator to TP3, the grid of the first IF amplifier. From this point, we can move the sweep signal in turn to each grid until we find the defective stage. Once the stage is isolated, we can go to our voltage and resistance check.

A problem in the color demodulator circuits can be isolated with similar techniques. The circuit of Fig. 6-22 shows the chroma demodulator in a Setchell Carlson 2900 receiver. By connecting a color-bar generator to the receiver antenna terminals, we can check the output waveforms at the red, blue, and green amplifiers (terminals 7, 9, and 10); typical waveforms are shown in Fig. 6-23. A scope with a demodulator probe is used. The chroma and chroma oscillator signals are fed to terminals 1, 3, and 4 and applied to the balanced demodulator diodes, D751 through D754. The B minus Y and R minus Y signals come from these demodulators while G minus Y is obtained by mixing the red and blue. So a defect in D751 or D752 can cause a loss of blue and green at the output, while a defect in D753 or D754 can cause a loss of red and green at the output.

One of the circuits that can cause a number of problems in a color receiver is the AFC (Automatic Frequency Control) circuit. Its purpose is to control horizontal sync or stability. Some of the problems caused by a faulty AFC circuit

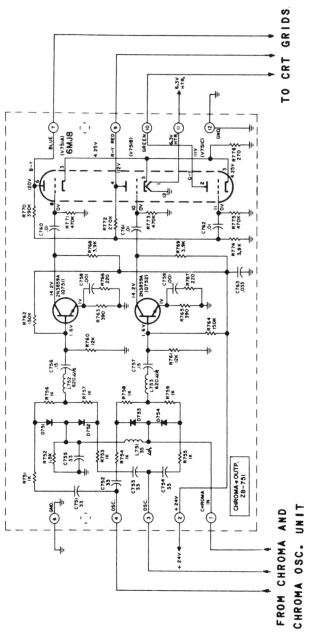

Fig. 6-22. Schematic diagram of the chroma output circuit in a Setchell Carlson 2900 color receiver. (Courtesy Setchell Carlson)

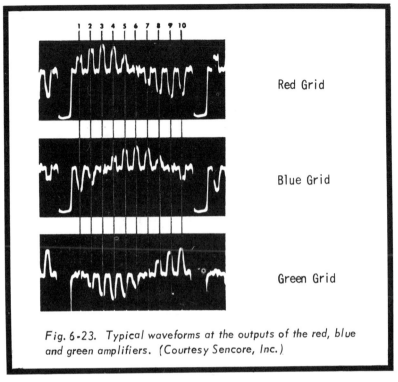

Fig. 6-23. Typical waveforms at the outputs of the red, blue and green amplifiers. (Courtesy Sencore, Inc.)

are horizontal pulling, poor width, a loss of raster and loss of horizontal sync. Fig. 6-24 shows a partial schematic of a horizontal AFC, oscillator, and output circuit. Dual diode DD501 is a conventional phase detector which controls the frequency of V501, the horizontal multivibrator. The sync input to the phase detector comes from the sync separator in the video amplifier stage.

A scope is the best test instrument for checking these circuits. If the problem is one of sync, waveform checks at the phase detector should be made first. If the problem is a lack of width or raster, check the oscillator and drive circuits first. With a direct probe connect the scope's vertical input to the grid of the horizontal output tube to check the drive waveform. Set the scope sweep at one-half the oscillator frequency or 7875 Hz. The waveform should appear as a sawtooth. Check the manufacturer's specifications for proper level and waveform. If the waveform is weak, missing, or distorted, pull out the trusty multi-meter and check voltages and components in the oscillator circuit. If the problem is

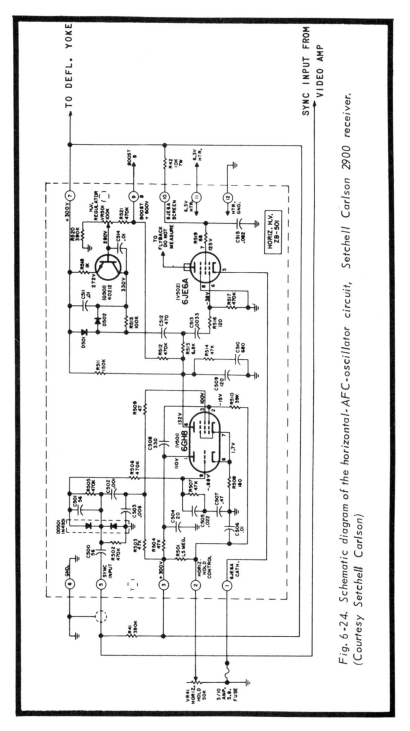

Fig. 6-24. Schematic diagram of the horizontal-AFC-oscillator circuit, Setchell Carlson 2900 receiver. (Courtesy Setchell Carlson)

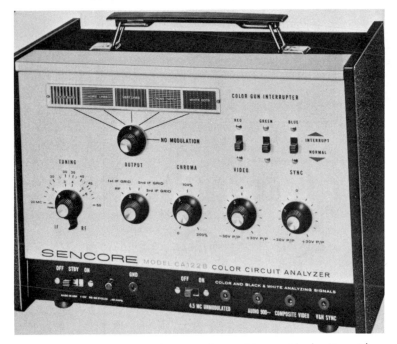

Fig. 6-25. Color circuit analyzer can be used for troubleshooting video, IF, RF, and sync circuits. (Courtesy Sencore, Inc.)

sync, check the sync input waveform (pin 5). The sync waveform should be approximately the same frequency as that at the horizontal grid, 7875 Hz. It, too, should be similar to a sawtooth.

Signal-carrying circuit troubles can be isolated with an instrument such as that shown in Fig. 6-25. This unit, along with many other analysts and sweep generators, provides a composite video output signal which can be fed directly to a video detector or video amplifier. In this way, a technician can troubleshoot the entire video chain from detector to picture tube. To do this, again referring to the manufacturer's manual, feed a signal to the video detector and check the grid(s) and outputs of each stage with a scope. The scope is connected through a low-capacity probe for troubleshooting these circuits and should be set to view a 30-Hz signal at a low voltage (2 volts p-p). A loss of signal or abnormal waveform at any stage isolates the problem to that area.

CHAPTER 7

Audio Servicing Instruments

Audio equipment servicing is a comparatively new field. Audio circuitry used to be considered just something hung on a radio to make the signals louder, and occasionally to act as an amplifier for the phonograph plugged into the jack. There were a few "high-class" amplifiers, but they were not widely used by the public. And, of course, we had the public address systems. But then it was easy to get defective audio equipment back into operation using the same service methods developed for other electronic equipment, and the question of quality seldom came up.

Those days are gone forever. Audio is now an exacting branch of electronic service, and we find such instruments as sine/square-wave generators (Fig. 7-1 and 7-2), harmonic or distortion analyzers, and intermodulation meters on the bench of the audio service technician—instruments that were formerly seen only in laboratories. Audio equipment is not difficult to repair. It usually involves injecting an audio signal source to the input and watching the amplified output on a scope or reading some value on a meter. However, audio equipment owners can be difficult people to please. More than one technician has been faced with what to him was a perfect amplifier, brought in for "repair" by its owner. High-fidelity equipment has to be right—often beyond the technician's ability to judge by ear. To insure perfection, special equipment is necessary. Much of it consists of meters, generators, etc., that could have been described under the classifications in earlier chapters, but because of the special nature of audio work they are grouped together here where we can talk about how to use them.

Before going into specialized equipment, let's see what

Fig. 7-1. A typical bench-type sine/square–wave generator.

Fig. 7-2. This sine/square–wave generator uses 8 transistors and a zener diode. It has separate level controls for sine and square waves.

Fig. 7-3. A sensitive AC VTVM is needed for some tests.

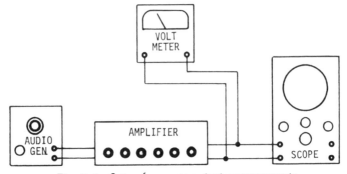

Fig. 7-4. Setup for power output measurements.

we can do with the ordinary fixed audio frequency (usually 400-450 Hz) of the bench signal generator described in Chapter 5. It produces a fairly good sine wave that can be varied in amplitude from practically zero to about 10 volts into a high impedance. It has one weakness—its fixed frequency. We can find out if the amplifier is doing its job only at 400 Hz. If it is a high-quality amplifier this knowledge is significant. Barring a defective component or old tubes, normal output and waveform at this frequency means it is probably in excellent working condition and will perform well over the entire spectrum. But if there is distortion, it may be an indication of serious weaknesses at the high and low extremes and we will need more sophisticated equipment to deal with it.

MEASURING OUTPUT

One thing we can do readily is check power output. The standard approach is to terminate the amplifier with a resistor rather than a speaker. The resistor must have the same value as the speaker in both resistance and power rating. For checking at one frequency, however, you can use the speaker. Hook up the audio generator, amplifier, scope and AC voltmeter (Fig. 7-3) as in Fig. 7-4. Adjust the scope frequency to get two or three sine-wave cycles on the screen. The audio generator should be turned well up. Set the amplifier controls to get a pattern like 7-5A.

A   **B**

Fig. 7-5. Undistorted sine-wave pattern (A). The same pattern shows clipping at B.

Now turn up the amplifier gain until the waves begin to "clip" as at 7-5B. Note the AC reading. Turn down the scope gain and the generator output and turn the amplifier up again to the clipping point. If the amplifier clips at the same output voltage, you have eliminated the generator and scope as possible causes of the clipping.

The undistorted power output of the amplifier is the power at the point where clipping just begins. The actual power is found by squaring the output voltage and dividing by the speaker resistance (P equals E^2/R). Thus, if your AC output is 20 volts and the speaker impedance is 8 ohms, the power is 20 x 20, or 400, divided by 8 or 50 watts. Generally the amplifier is said to have so many watts output over some frequency range and this is often given in terms of db. Most of the AC VTVMs today have scales directly calibrated in both watts and db. Many of the hi-fi specifications are indicated by the manufacturer in terms of db. The AC VTVM can be connected to a hi-fi amplifier's output terminals and read directly in watts. However, the meter must be matched to the amplifier's output impedance.

Another approach—phase-angle checking—can be used to measure maximum power. (If you have a variable-frequency audio generator, it will measure a number of other things, too.) Hook up the equipment as in Fig. 7-6. If you keep the

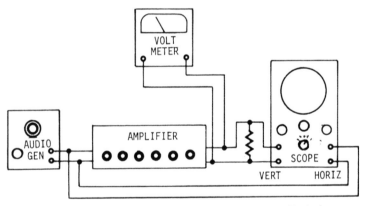

Fig. 7-6. Another setup for power output measurement. With this setup you can also check phase angle.

sweep on INT, there will no be change in the pattern. But if you move it to EXT and apply the same test signal to the horizontal input, you can get a pattern like Fig. 7-7A. Manipulate the audio output control on your signal generator, the amplifier gain, and the scope gain controls (both horizontal and vertical) till you get a straight line at an angle of 45°.

A little skill is needed in these adjustments—you don't want to turn any one of the four controls up to near maxi-

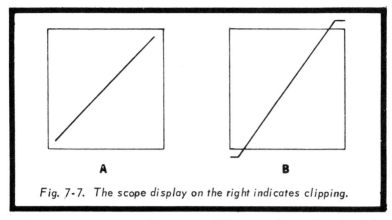

A B

Fig. 7-7. The scope display on the right indicates clipping.

mum or you may get distortion. When you have the straight line at 45°, the input to the horizontal and vertical plates is identical in signal strength and in phase. If the signal opens into an ellipse, the signals are not exactly in phase between the input and the output of the amplifier—there is phase shift in the amplifier. For our present tests, at 450Hz or so, we don't have to worry about a small amount of phase shift and can usually make a straight line with the help of the bass and treble controls.

Now turn up the amplifier gain control. Above a certain point the line on the scope will suddenly become distorted and take on the shape of Fig. 7-7B indicating that the amplifier is starting to clip. The AC output voltage ceases to go up as the input voltage is increased. The power output is again at

Fig. 7-8. A scope indication like this is not due to clipping; it's caused by plate saturation.

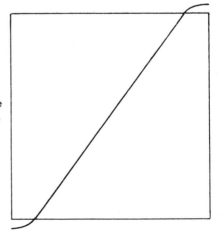

127

the point where a further increase in the amplifier gain starts to cause distortion. You may get another form of distortion, like Fig. 7-8. This is a sign of plate saturation instead of grid clipping—the tube just can't supply any more electrons. It shows up as a rounded curve instead of a sharp horizontal cut-off.)

SIGNAL TRACING

The audio portion of the bench generator is, of course, also a good instrument for signal injection to trace the signal through an amplifier. As in radio or TV servicing, you want to isolate the problem to one stage and then take necessary voltage and resistance measurements.

Assuming that you have first checked all connections to the amplifier, including the speaker, we can go into the amplifier circuit. The fastest way to break the amplifier problem down to one section is to put your finger or audio signal probe at the top of the volume control. No output here has quickly and locically isolated the problem to the section of the amplifier after the volume control.

Now move your audio signal to the input of the stage following the volume control. Don't overlook the fact that the volume control may be open. If you have no signal here, continue moving the test signal input toward the amplifier output, stage by stage. At some point you should have output. If you don't, better get out the multimeter and start checking voltage and resistance readings.

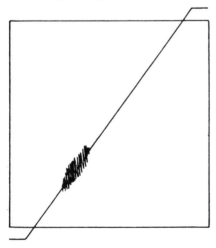

Fig. 7-9. Parasitic oscillation in an amplifier shows up like this.

In stereo amplifiers just one channel may become defective. If so it is serviced in the same way. If both channels go dead, check the circuit common to both channels first, such as the power supply.

Many amplifiers start oscillating when the gain is turned up beyond a certain point. This oscillation shows up as a fuzzy area on the scope trace (Fig. 7-9) with the test instruments connected as in Fig. 7-6. The pattern looks something like that made by a marker generator in TV servicing, but much broader than any good marker should be. Some amplifiers may oscillate, or "ring," only when certain frequencies are amplified and our fixed-frequency generator is unable to find these oscillations. We need something a little better— a variable-frequency audio generator.

THE AUDIO GENERATOR

The chief limitation of our bench AM-RF signal generator as an audio oscillator is that it can produce only one or two frequencies. But often an amplifier that is good at 300 Hz may not be perfect at 15,000 Hz or at 60 Hz. To find out what it will do at the lower and higher frequencies, we need an audio generator that covers this spectrum. The average audio sine-wave generator (or sine-wave portion of the sine-square-wave generator) produces signals from about 20 Hz up to the lower radio frequencies—100 kHz to 1 MHz in a few generators. It can be used for a large number of tests for which the fixed-frequency instrument is inadequate.

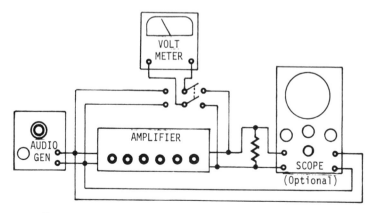

Fig. 7-10. Equipment setup for frequency response tests.

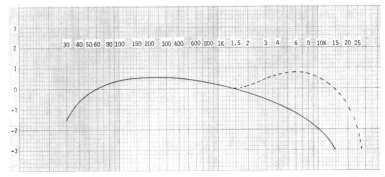

Fig. 7-11. Amplifier response curve. The dashed line shows the effect of the tone control.

Probably the most useful test to perform on a hi fi ampli-fier is the frequency response test. We know the output of our amplifier at 450 Hz from a previous test but do not know if it will do as well at 50 and 10,000 Hz. Failure to amplify signals of all frequencies equally well is frequency distortion and this is given in the manufacturer's specifications. To check the amplifier's frequency response, we can set up the equipment as in Fig. 7-10. The tone controls are set to the middle of their range to provide a "flat" response. Set the audio generator at 1,000 Hz (This is the frequency commonly used for reference) and turn the amplifier up to full output (the clipping level). Note the output on the AC voltmeter or VTVM. It is your reference voltage. Now, check the out-put at various frequencies by setting the generator at 20 Hz and slowly increasing the frequency to 20,000 Hz. Note the output voltage at each end of the frequency range. The

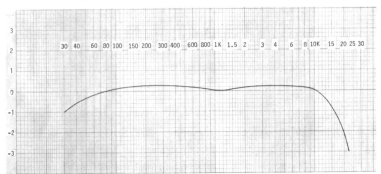

Fig. 7-12. This curve shows the results of adjusting the tone controls for equal response 100 and 10,000 Hz.

curves in Figs. 7-11 and 7-12 were made by measuring the output at approximately 23 evenly-spaced points from 30 to 30,000 Hz. When you get a set of readings relative to the 1000-Hz reading you can plot a curve. The values can be listed in volts, watts or db (decibels), depending on your meter. A table is provided in the Appendix to convert voltage to db.

Moderately good amplifiers today are almost absolutely flat between 20 and 20,000 Hz. The curve in Fig. 7-11 was made on an amplifier 10 years old. When new, it was rated absolutely flat from 20 Hz to 60 kHz. Even with the passage of time, it was down only 1 db at 30 Hz and 3 db at 15 kHz. Advancing the treble control (dashed line) brought the "flat" response range up to well past 15 kHz—only 2 db down at 25 kHz. A further experiment, in which treble, bass, and gain controls were adjusted to give the same gain (full output) at 100, 1,000 and 10,000 Hz, resulted in the curve of Fig. 7-12.

As we can see in Fig. 7-11, the amplifier output at 30 Hz is down 1.3 db (approximately). This means that at 30 Hz the output power is about three-fourths of full power which tells us that the amplifier is not "flat" down to 30 Hz. "Flat" response from 30 to 30,000 Hz indicates that the system will amplify all frequencies equally across the entire spectrum. In actual practice it would take an exceptional amplifier to do this. However, reasonably-priced units usually provide good response from 15 Hz to 15 kHz. And be sure you keep in mind that any hi-fi or stereo system is only as good as the speakers to which it is connected.

Remember the following precautions when making a test of amplifier frequency response. First, line voltage must be normal and steady. Changes in line voltage during a measurement can produce some unexpected effects. Second, the tone controls are to be set "flat" (mid-range). Third, terminate the speaker output in a proper resistance because the impedance of a speaker varies greatly over the audio range. Since it is necessary to be able to measure the input and output voltages accurately, the voltmeter must have an appropriate frequency range. Some audio generators have built-in output meters so a voltmeter is needed only across the amplifier output. If you have to measure both input and output levels you should use an AC VTVM.

THE AUDIO VOLTMETER

An audio voltmeter, also called an AC VTVM, is important in audio service work because it attains levels that can't be read on ordinary bench VTVM or VOM. With a lowest range of .01 volt or less you can use it to follow a signal right from the phono pickup all the way through the amplifier. Used in the circuit of Fig. 7-10, for example, it will easily handle the smallest input signal and the largest signal output.

The audio voltmeter is particularly useful in troubleshooting. You simply follow the signal through the amplifier and notice where the gain seems lower than normal, (The scope is somewhat less sensitive, or at least harder to read for small changes, but has the advantage that you can watch the waveform as well as the gain.) If you are working with a stereo amplifier follow the signals down the two channels until you come to the point where they differ noticeably. That is the point where one of them is wrong. A big difference between the voltages on the two channels, for example, might indicate a shorted coupling capacitor, bad tube or transistor, or off-value resistors. Especially watch for this in transistorized units where bias voltages are critical. Check back to the point where the signal (AC voltage) is correct, then track down the defective component by tube or transistor checking and voltage and resistance tests.

The AC voltmeter is a useful instrument for adjusting balance in pushpull stages, too. Pushpull outputs are supposed to be opposite in phase but equal in level to cancel out distortion. But differences in tubes (or sections of the same tube) coupling capacitors or resistors, etc., may put different voltages on the pushpull grids and cause a change in the amplifying ability of one of them as compared to the other. Some output transformer manufacturers make the primary a continuous winding instead of winding it in two separate sections or several "pies." Even though there are the same number of turns on each half, the outer half will have more wire and more resistance. As a result, the balance controls that are used on many amplifiers to equalize the cathode cur-

132

rents give you a static balance but will not do much to help AC balance.

To check and adjust the output balance connect the AC voltmeter across one side of the output transformer primary and (from one plate to center tap) note the voltage produced by a steady signal input from an audio generator. Then connect it across the other side and compare the output voltages. Use the balancing control to make the two voltages equal. This check is best made with the amplifier delivering nearly full output. It is a good idea to check it again at low output. If the balance is far different at different output levels, it may be worth while to replace the tubes. To get a check on the quality of the output transformer, compare the balance at 100 Hz and 10 kHz. (This assumes that you balanced originally at 450 or 1,000 Hz.)

The audio voltmeter is often useful as a sensitive audio signal tracer, since many models have a sensitive audio amplifier. With a pair of phones in the output jack, very weak signals can be heard. For example, in organ servicing, the voltmeter-amplifier can be plugged across the oscillator output (or successively across several outputs, if more than one is not working). The signal, if any, can be heard clearly and traced to the point where it disappears.

An AC VTVM is often used as a wattmeter as mentioned earlier. (Since it is generally used to measure the wattage output of an audio amplifier, a sensitive audio type is not necessary.) If you know the voltage across a given resistance, you can figure out the wattage (P equals E^2/R). Or you can calculate the current through R and multiply that value by the voltage. So we simply connect the AC voltmeter across the output resistor, as in Figs. 7-6 and 7-10. Amplifier output impedances are (almost) always 4, 8, or 16 ohms. Unfortunately, few resistors are made in these exact values. Some audio test instruments have built-in resistors for taking power readings. If not, try to find a resistor which is reasonably close. If you are likely to be working with medium-power equipment you can connect resistors in parallel or series combinations to get the desired values. For example, two 8-ohm, 10-watt resistors in parallel will give you 4 ohms at 20 watts. For larger powers, and especially for transistor amplifiers where you might wish to measure the power on the

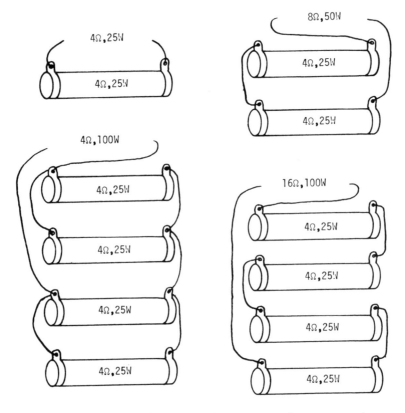

Fig. 7-13. Resistors can be connected in a variety of ways to match any output impedance and power.

4- and 8-ohm outputs, it might be better to buy 4-ohm, 25-watt units, which are a standard size and easily obtainable. They can be hooked up a variety of ways for different maximum power output and resistance values as shown in Fig. 7-13.

INTERMODULATION ANALYSIS

The most troublesome problem in high-fidelity amplifier design is intermodulation distortion. It is usually checked with an intermodulation analyzer. This instrument measures the effect that one signal passing through the amplifier may have on other signals. A perfect amplifier amplifies all signals of all frequencies and amplitudes exactly alike and all the signals pass through without affecting any others. But if there is any difference in the way the amplifier handles different signals, they start to modulate each other, producing new frequencies (harmonics) much the same way the intermediate frequency in a superheterodyne is produced by the intermodulation of the received carrier frequency and a local oscillator frequency. An organ can be played to produce signals at 100 Hz or it can produce harmonics at 200, 300 and 400 Hz, through special circuits. But if there is any nonlinearity in the organ's 100-Hz signal, it will produce new intermodulation signals at 900 and 1100 Hz (sum and difference frequencies, Fig. 7-14). These "fuzz" up the 100-Hz note of the organ and make the amplifier sound poor

But this is not the worst of it. Organ harmonics (the 200-Hz one, for instance) will produce additional sum and difference frequencies as well. And all the other harmonics (very strong in most organ voices) intermodulate not only the fundamental 100-Hz note but its harmonics, also. Even the spurious frequencies produced by intermodulation can intermodulate each other in some cases! When the musical expert speaks of a "clean" amplifier—when he listens for single instruments in an orchestral record—he is speaking of (or listening for) amplification without intermodulation.

The intermodulation analyzer (Fig. 7-15) puts two carefully-measured signals of different frequencies into the amplifier in a ratio of 4 to 1. Then it measures the amount one has modulated the other. Both signals are pure sine waves—one at 60 Hz is commonly used for the lower signal and one at several thousand Hz for the high signal. These signals are usually generated by the instrument.

To use the instrument, you set the controls so that the higher-frequency signal is about one quarter as strong as the 60-Hz one (4-to-1 ratio). These mixed signals are fed through

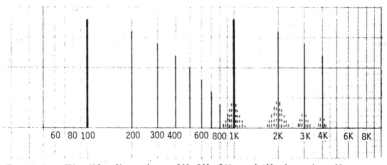

| | 60 | 80 | 100 | | 200 | 300 | 400 | | 600 | 800 | 1K | | 2K | | 3K | 4K | | 6K | 8K |

Fig. 7-14. The "fuzz" marks at 1K, 2K, 3K, and 4K show the effects of intermodulation distortion.

135

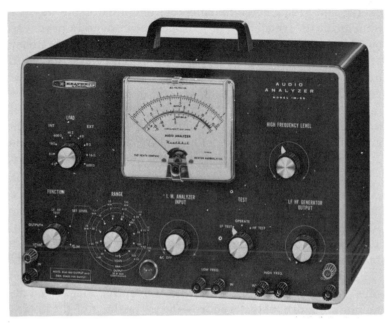

Fig. 7-15. This Heathkit audio analyzer serves a number of functions: intermodulation analyzer, AC voltmeter, and wattmeter.

the amplifier and back into the analyzer which is now set to measure distortion. It goes first through a high-pass filter which takes out the 60-Hz part of the signal. The high-frequency signal then goes through a detector which leaves only the 60-Hz modulation (as the speech and music modulation is all that is left when a radio signal is detected, or demodulated). Intermodulation (modulation) of the high-frequency (2 kHz to 8 kHz) signal is indicated on the meter in terms of percentage.

The actual measurement of intermodulation is more complex than most other audio measurements. The instrument itself contains the two signal generators that produce the high and low audio tones. One meter is used for everything. It is first switched to set the strength of the low-frequency (60 Hz) tone, which is accomplished by adjusting the output control till the meter reads full-scale with the 60-Hz signal.

The combined output is applied to the amplifier input and the analyzer input. Some analyzers contain built-in load resistors (4, 8, 16 and 600 ohms) and it is necessary only to switch to the correct load for the amplifier. With others it is necessary to connect a resistor of the correct value across the amplifier output. To use the analyzer warm everything up and adjust the amplifier controls for full output and presumably "flat" response (tone controls often have a strong effect on intermodulation and sometimes it is desirable to check intermodulation with one or both of them turned well up). Also, be certain that the amplifier under test is "flat" within the frequency ranges of the two signals to be used. Never use accessory test units that have a 3-wire grounded plug. This will just give you incorrect readings. Grounded and shielded leads between units are advisable because any signal the analyzer picks up will be added to the distortion. Follow the manufacturer's instructions for using the analyzer, always.

The analyzer is useful for other tests too. It may be connected across any audio or preamp stage where you may suspect intermodulation distortion. A high-impedance input position is normally provided for that purpose. You can even check a phono pickup by using an intermodulation test record as a signal source.

THE AUDIO ANALYZER

Since the intermodulation analyzer contains an AC voltmeter, and since the resistors needed for wattage measurements are also included in many models, it is not surprising that a combination instrument which will measure voltage and wattage as well as intermodulation is available. The Heathkit Analyzer in Fig. 7-15 is typical. Instruments of this type, called "audio analyzers," are very useful as an all-round audio test instrument. A few additional positions of the function switch are used with an ingenious "voltage corrector" which varies the meter reading according to the output load so that a correct wattage is indicated for all values of amplifier output impedance. Wattage readings in a typical instrument may range from 0.15 mw to 150 watts. The VTVM scales may go from .01 volt to 300 volts with a frequency response within 1 db from 10 Hz to 100 kHz.

HARMONIC DISTORTION METERS

The more advanced experimenter, laboratory worker, or design engineer may not be satisfied with simply being able to measure the quantity of distortion in an amplifier. He wants to know where in the audio sprctrum the distortion is. Obviously, if most of the distortion is below 100 Hz, his problems are entirely different than if it were practically all in the high-frequency range. Even in servicing an amplifier it is often convenient and useful to know what kind of distortion (high- or low-frequency) you have. The "harmonic distortion meter" (or the more expensive "wave analyzer") answers that question.

A harmonic distortion analyzer is connected to the output of the amplifier being tested. A sinewave generator is connected to the input and a signal of any frequency in the audio range put through the amplifier. The analyzer is tuned to the same frequency and a level control set to give a specific reading on the meters—100, for example.

Like the intermodulation meter, the instrument works by nulling out an input signal and reading what is left. The harmonic distortion meter nulls out the very signal that the generator supplies to the amplifier. If a 5,000-Hz signal is supplied by the generator, for example, the analyzer is adjusted to take out the 5,000-Hz frequency. This is done by a bridge circuit in the analyzer that is tuned to balance out the fundamental frequency fed to it, while offering a high impedance to signals of any other frequency. (This is a Wein bridge used in many types of test instruments.) When the bridge is switched in to take out the input signal (5,000 Hz in our example) the meter drops from 100 to indicate the amount of signal left. This is caused by signals other than the one the equipment is supposed to be amplifying. Harmonics of the original signal make up the greater part of these signals, together with any noise in the amplifier or the test equipment itself. If the output was orginally set at 100 on the meter, the reading produced by the remaining signals will indicate the distortion and noise in percentage, as with the intermodulation meter.

A wave analyzer can be used to inspect a signal in detail. A wave analyzer is a selective voltmeter that can be tuned to any frequency of a given signal. Thus, if you have a note of, say, 450 Hz, it is possible to check the strength of the second harmonic at 900 Hz and compare it with the signal strength of the third harmonic at 1350 Hz. Intermodulation signals can be determined and measured by tuning across the spectrum. If the strength of the fundamental signal is set to give a full-scale reading (100) on the meter, the various harmonics and modulation products can be read in percentages, as with the intermodulation meter and harmonic analyzer.

While these instruments could be useful to the service technician as well as to the design engineer, their cost keeps them off the average bench. For the practical worker, the audio analyzer is an excellent device. Used with an oscilloscope and a sine/square-wave generator they enable him to solve practically any audio problem he may run up against.

THE SQUARE-WAVE GENERATOR

A square-wave generator is the universal audio test instrument. It invariably includes a sine-wave generator, and so can be used for all the purposes already described for an audio generator. In addition, it produces square waves— signals that rise immediately (in a tenth of a microsecond or so) from zero to full output, remain at full output for half a cycle, then drop and immediately rise to full output in the opposite direction. See Fig. 7-16. Square waves can usually be produced at a rate varying from about 20 Hz to the lower radio frequencies—200 kHz.

The square wave is considered to be made up of a large number of frequencies or harmonics—a fundamental at a very low frequency and its odd harmonics, as seen in Fig. 7-17. This may or may not be literally true, since it has been

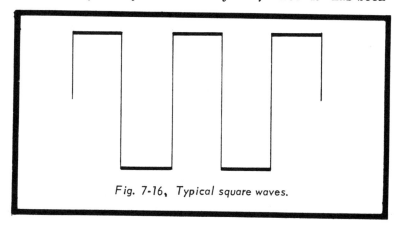

Fig. 7-16, Typical square waves.

pointed out that an excellent square wave can be produced with a dry cell and a switch, using nothing but DC. The important thing to us is that an amplifier fed square waves behaves exactly as if it had received a composite waveform made up of a large number of frequencies, ranging from the lowest to the highest. Thus, we can use a square-wave generator to check through an amplifier instantaneously, without varying the frequency over wide ranges.

If you are a bit doubtful about that, look at Fig. 7-17 again. It shows a very simplified picture of a square wave—the fundamental and fifth harmonic (Fig. 7-17B). Notice that the low-frequency fundamental "holds the center up" while the high-frequency component is the one that "keeps the corners straight." So it should be expected that if the amplifier could not reproduce low notes the center of the square wave would droop as in Fig. 7-17C. (Imagine the fundamental only half as high as in 7-17B). And if the higher frequencies were not being amplified, the "square" wave would look more like Fig. 7-17D.

If an amplifier can reproduce the straight "leading edge" (the left edge of the wave) it responds fast enough to handle any musical note. (Notice we said "amplifier." Some speakers start slow and continue to produce sound after the signal has stopped.) And if the amplifier can maintain its response over the period of the half wave, it can handle low notes, down to about one-tenth the frequency to which the generator is set.

The square-wave generator is easy to use and the results easy to interpret. Frequency is usually set with a dial (controlling a variable capacitor) and a multiplier switch, which selects the ranges. With the switch at X1, simply read the dial directly; for X10 multiply the dial reading 10 times (60 Hz on the dial is actually 600 Hz) and so on. An attenuator with coarse and fine output control is an important feature.

To check frequency response, connect the square-wave generator output to the amplifier input, cut the signal down with the attenuator to where there'll be no danger of overload, and attach the scope to the output. Again, instead of a speaker use a resistor of the correct value and with a high enough wattage rating.

For some tests you may want to have the speaker connected.

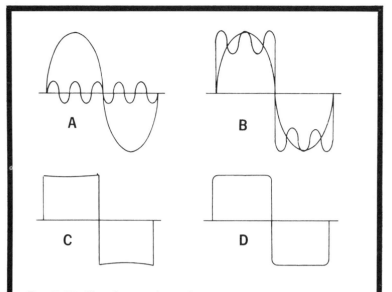

Fig. 7-17. Waveform A shows the components of a square wave - the fundamental and fifth harmonic. Waveform B shows how they combine to form a square wave. If the fundamental is weak (C), the tops and bottom are bowed. If the harmonic is weak (D) the corners are rounded.

Of course, its effect on the amplifier differs at different frequencies, whereas the resistance load is constant. (That's why resistors are used for most tests). Set the scope to show two or more square-wave cycles at the frequency you intend to use. It is common to use 200 Hz to show the performance of an amplifier from about 20 to around 20,000 Hz.

Inspect the pattern on the screen. If the amplifier's high-frequency response is poor, or if it shows trouble with transients, its output will not be able to rise as fast as the generator pulse, and the leading edges will be rounded as in Fig. 7-18A. If it's weak on the low frequencies, it won't hold up during the steady part of the wave, and the top will be tilted or concave as in Fig. 7-18B. Oscillation or ringing will show up as waves on top of the square wave (Fig. 7-18C). Some ringing may be caused by the speaker in a poorly-damped output circuit and won't be seen in a resistance-loaded amplifier. Some patterns showing phase shift, as well as oscillation, are shown in Fig. 2-1.

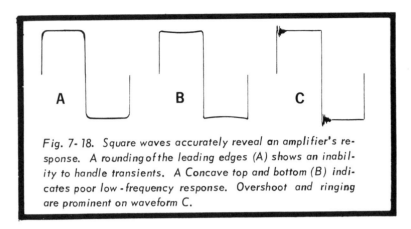

*Fig. 7- 18. Square waves accurately reveal an amplifier's re-
sponse. A rounding of the leading edges (A) shows an inabil-
ity to handle transients. A Concave top and bottom (B) indicates poor low - frequency response. Overshoot and ringing
are prominent on waveform C.*

FM STEREO TEST INSTRUMENTS

Stereo FM introduces a number of possible new problems
for the technician. Several circuits unknown in any other
equipment have to be checked and aligned. And alignment
in multiplex circuits does not mean adjusting the frequency
to within a few cycles per second as it does in some so-
called "critical" circuits—it means adjusting it not only to
the cycle but phasing it so that the beginning of each cycle
in the equipment is exactly synchronized with the beginning
of the same cycle in the transmitted signal.

First of all, stereo FM multiplex receivers will pick up
what is called a Subsidiary Communications Authority (SCA)
channel which is used for "storecasting" by some stations
along with regular stereo programming. It has nothing to do
with the stereo you are servicing, but the signal must be
trapped out. Then there are 19-kHz and 38-kHz signals,
used to supply a carrier for part of the stereo signal. The
circuits handling these signals not only have to be set and
peaked correctly, but phase-adjusted to the multiplex signal coming in on a band centered at 38 kHz. There are also
a few other traps which are intended to keep the 19- and
38-kHz signals in their places, and especially out of the output circuits.

The FM stereo generator (in some types referred to as a
stereo FM signal simulator) supplies signals that make it
possible to adjust those circuits. See Fig. 7-19. The average FM multiplex stereo generator can supply these signals
as modulation on a stereo FM carrier, usually at or around

100 MHz, or directly in the form they would be at the output of an FM receiver discriminator. In some generators the 100-MHz signal can be swept. Thus, the generator can be used for regular FM receiver IF and detector-discriminator alignment. Some so-called multiplex generators do not supply an RF signal; thus are usable only for aligning the multiplex portion of the receiver.

The method of using the generator depends to some extent on the design of the multiplex circuitry. There are two main types: matrix and switching. There are also differences in the way the 38-kHz carrier is produced for insertion on the multiplex signal which is transmitted with its carrier suppressed. The 19-kHz pilot signal may simply be amplified considerably then doubled to 38 kHz and used as carrier, or the equipment may have a 19-kHz oscillator which is synchronized to the pilot signal then doubled to supply the 38-kHz carrier. The more common method is to use a 38-kHz oscillator and use the 19-kHz pilot signal to synchronize it.

All the circuits and methods of synchronization make for differences in alignment practice. Obviously, the manufacturer's instructions are needed as in TV alignment. There are still a few of the once very popular multiplex adapters around. Since they are now semi-orphans it may be hard to locate any instructions. If you can locate the various adjustments and traps, possibly the best approach is to start

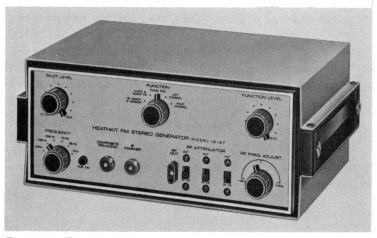

Fig. 7-19. This Heathkit stereo generator furnishes a variety of signals from 100 MHz down to 400 Hz.

by adjusting the 67-kHz SCA trap or traps for minimum output. Then, align the 19-kHz transformer for greatest output, afterward the 38-kHz transformer. The separation or stereo-balance control is then set for maximum signal on the channel being supplied with a signal (LEFT CHANNEL or RIGHT CHANNEL output of the generator) and for minimum on the other channel. Now, set the 19- and 38-kHz traps, if any, for minimum output. This provides the best channel separation for stereo. The instructions in the signal generator manual will be helpful here, though they may not suggest the same approach as the one given above.

FM Channel Separation Adjustment

Generally, when aligning a stereo multiplex receiver, the 100-MHz generator output is used. If the receiver has a multiplex adapter, the audio composite signal is used. Manufacturer's instructions for alignment vary somewhat, so it is best to follow his suggestions. However, a typical procedure is to connect the generator to the receiver antenna after the test generator has warmed up. Some generators have built-in meters with load resistors and test leads to replace the system speakers. In this case, the generator meters are used in place of the speakers. If not, an AC VTVM or scope should be connected across each speaker. A dual-trace scope would be ideal! If only one test instrument is used, it will have to be swapped back and forth between left- and right-channel outputs. Turn the receiver on and tune it to 100 MHz, with the generator set to provide signals to both channels. Then, adjust the receiver to achieve channel separation according to the manufacturer's specifications. Adjust the receiver separation controls for minimum left-channel output on the right channel and vice-versa.

You may find some trace of 19-kHz and 38-kHz signal in the output, but in modern receivers they should be low enough not to cause a problem because they are too high in frequency to hear. If a scope is used, the left and right channels should be pure sine waves.

38-kHz Subcarrier Adjustment

Any misalignment of the 38-kHz subcarrier can cause distortion and poor separation, especially in receivers using matrix circuits. To check and align the 38-kHz subcarrier phase, set up the equipment just as you did to adjust the channel separation. Refer to the manufacturer's manual and adjust the receiver for <u>maximum</u> signal at both channel outputs. It may be necessary to readjust the channel-separation controls after this type of alignment. Another method of alignment is to connect a scope at each output and adjust the receiver for a pure 1200-Hz sinewave.

The 19-kHz and 38-kHz filter and oscillator adjustments should also be made following the manufacturer's instructions. Usually the 19-kHz pilot signal is filtered and doubled to get the 38-kHz subcarrier frequency which is reinserted. As mentioned earlier, some receivers use two oscillators, with the 19-kHz oscillator providing sychronization. Align the 67-kHz (SCA) trap by connecting a VTVM or scope across it and tuning for minimum with a 67-kHz signal input.

LOW-COST SWEEP GENERATOR

One model RF generator, intended for general radio and TV service work, contains features that will make it very interesting to the hi-fi service technician. The RCA WR-50B (Fig. 7-20) contains sweep circuitry for aligning not only

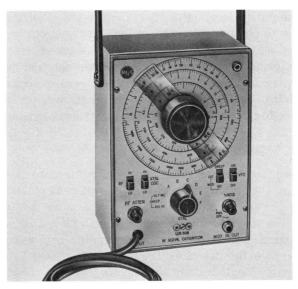

Fig. 7-20. This RCA generator provides sweep signals for AM and FM tests.

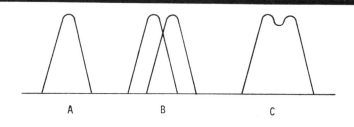

Fig. 7-21. Response curve of a peaked IF transformer (A). If each winding is tuned to a slightly different frequency (B) it produces an overall curve with two peaks (C).

FM IFs, but AM IFs as well. Though the first sweep generators (wobulators) were made to align high-quality AM radios, it has been many years since the audio man could get a generator designed to work with 20-kHz wide IFs. A generator that will sweep that spectrum—as well as handle FM IFs—is welcome.

In aligning the AM IF, the object is to get an IF curve as flat topped as possible, centered of course, on 455 kHz. With present-day IFs, this can best be done by tuning the primary and secondary to slightly different frequencies, so that the peak widens (Fig. 7-21). For FM IF alignment the aim is to obtain a smooth, broad, rounded curve. By inserting a 10.7-MHz crystal in the socket provided in this generator, this curve may be made symmetrical around the center frequency of 10.7 MHz. The sweep is also useful in examining the IF curve for abnormal shapes. A tendency to peak, for example, would indicate probable regeneration.

CURING TROUBLE IN HI FI EQUIPMENT

If distortion is the trouble, the usual component checks will turn up the cause, once the general area of trouble is known. But since distortion is often a more subtle trouble than those we have been running down in TV and RF circuits, more care is needed. Tubes, for example, are more important in high-fidelity circuitry than in most other electronic equipment. Replace them with known good tubes as a check, even though they may show up favorable on a tube tester. Some hi-fi enthusiasts replace their output tubes regularly,

146

"whether they need it or not." Tubes that are not perfectly matched at all signal levels can distort and upset the balance in pushpull stages. Re-balance the output stages if necessary. Usually when replacing pushpull transistors, they are replaced in matched pairs to eliminate imbalance, The use of pushpull cancels certain types of distortion and reduces hum markedly, but the unnecessary use of unbalanced components destroys some of the advantage of pushpull operation.

Wrong biasing is another common cause of hi-fi distortion, espcially in transistor circuits. Check the cathode (base) resistor first, then measure the cathode voltage and compare it with the voltage given in the service manual. Ideally, it should be possible to measure cathode or base current at various signal levels, but you can use a voltmeter on the plate or collector terminal to get some information. If a tube or transistor has too much bias, positive alternations of input voltage can increase the current more than the negative alternations can decrease it. This causes output current to rise during moderately strong input signals and this increase in current can be detected as a slight drop in voltage.

If there is not enough bias, the opposite may be expected; negative alternations of grid voltage reduce the plate current more than the equal positive alternations can increase it. A properly biased tube should draw a steady current up to the overload point. This does not apply to pushpull output tubes. Most output stages are operated Class AB, which means that they are supposed to draw more current as the signal increases.

Feedback circuits introduce their own brand of complications. Check the feedback resistors and capacitors, if any, as a first step. Notice differences in quality and volume with feedback connected and disconnected.

Hum is also a special problem in audio circuitry. It exists in all electronic equipment, but has a better chance to compete with the signal in audio—and especially high-fidelity—equipment. You certainly have heard the rules about grounding. Apply them, and watch for hidden resistances or unsuspected loops. In a recent difficult problem hum in a phonograph turntable, we went so far as to shield the motor wiring. In doing so, it was necessary to remove a shielding hood over the terminal strip. The screw that held the hood to the metal bottom of the turntable—and incidentally, to which the shield lead from the pickup arm is connected—was found to be slightly loose. Ohmmeter tests showed zero ohms as far as could be read on an ohmmeter. But to a voltage of a few millivolts the resistance must have seemed very real because the screw came up through the bottom to a nut that was pretty well covered by the shield; it escaped detection. Tightening it reduced the hum to a negligible level.

As you can readily see from the above examples, troubleshooting follows essentially the lines laid down in previous chapters: localize the trouble, then find the component that is causing it.

CHAPTER 8

The Capacitor Checker

A capacitor tester, properly used, is a real time saver. But even more than that, it helps you to do a better job. Many technicians are aware of its importance in checking filter capacitors. You can determine the exact capacitance as well as whether or not the power factor has begun to increase. True, the practical man often finds it quicker to bridge the suspected capacitor with a new one, but that method has weaknesses. A "filter" may still have quite a bit of capacitance, yet a high power factor may not be evident during a temporary bridging (receiver oscillation over certain parts of the radio spectrum. for example). And high leakage may go undetected. The checker not only digs out those defects, but spots capacitors that are just beginning to show power factor or leakage not great enough to have any noticeable effect at the moment but definite enough to warn the technician to replace it before real trouble shows up.

The capacitor values used in many circuit functions in electronic equipment vary rather widely. Grid return capacitors in a radio receiver RF circuit, for instance, could be almost any value from about 500 pfd to 10,000 mfd and still do a good job. There are many other functions where the capacitor will continue to work after a fashion, unless it's open or dead shorted. But there are places—particularly in TV circuits— where a capacitor that gets too far away from its rated value can upset everything. Frequency-control circuit capacitor tolerances must be closer than that required for bypass purposes. And a capacitor that has to charge up to a certain voltage during a single horizontal sweep, for example, has to be close to specs. The frequency of a multivibrator depends on the product of the resistance and capacitance in the frequency-controlling circuit, and a slight change in the capacitor immediately produces an equivalent change in frequency.

149

A capacitor that drops below specs is most likely to give trouble. You could replace most .01-mfd bypass capacitors with a 1 mfd with no noticeable results. But too much capacitance is serious in some circuits. In the charging circuit just mentioned, too big a capacitor would mean too low voltage at the end of the sweep. Even in the simple radio AVC circuit, too much capacitance can mean that control does not follow the signal close enough. The AVC does not go on till after the first loud crash of a passage and then it drains away slowly during the following pianissimo (Some amateurs remove the AVC capacitor entirely, letting the receiver come to full sensitivity between each individual dot and dash.) This could be very unpleasant on speech. You would get clipping since the signal strength would be cut down drastically on a single word. Imagine what that would do to an orator striving for dramatic effect!

Coupling capacitors can be critical, too. A high-fidelity amplifier can lose bass notes if a coupler loses capacitance. And if it is replaced with an oversize unit, the high-frequency "roll-off" and the phase changes through the feedback circuit (all factors that have been worked out mathematically by the designer) can be affected.

The average capacitance tester is equipped to check for leadage, although leakage can of course be checked with the multimeter. But many times a capacitor that shows practically no leakage on an ohmmeter (which may use a 1.5- or 3-volt battery) is unmistakably faulty when tested for leakage at its working voltage. The reason, of course, is that an ohmmeter does not duplicate the working voltage applied to the capacitor in the actual circuit. Also, capacitors of lower ratings (those used in transistor circuits) can sometimes be "healed" by an ohmmeter and show up as a problem later. Many "capacimeters" can also check capacitors in a circuit. This is a timesaver—if used with caution and judgment.

CRUDE CAPACITOR CHECKERS

The ohmmeter section of the multi-meter is often used for rough capacitor checking. A large capacitor is a momentary dead short. The meter pointer goes to zero ohms, then climbs slowly to a very high resistance as the capacitor charges. A smaller capacitor will cause a quick "kick" of the pointer to-

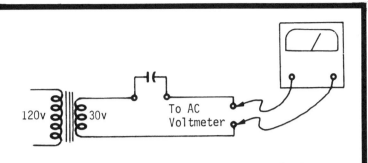

Fig. 8·1. Capacitance can be measured with an AC voltmeter. If it is adjusted to full scale and an impedance inserted in the circuit the reading will drop. The meter can be calibrated with the help of known capacitors. Be sure to use a transformer that isolates the instrument from the AC line and keep the voltages low enough to be safe.

ward a lower ohms figure, with an immediate return to near infinity (if the capacitor is good). Even very small capacitors (down to about 100 pfd) can be checked, though not measured, with the ohmmeter. If the pointer kicks, the capacitor is not open. An indication can be obtained on capacitors too small to measure otherwise by trying them first in one direction (which charges the capacitor) then the other. Thus the capacitor discharge is added to the charging current, doubling the indication on the meter.

A less crude method is to use the multi-meter as an AC voltmeter. One of the earliest multi-meters had a scale marked directly in microfarads, and one of the latest VTVMs has one. If the AC voltmeter is set to 30 volts, for example, and 30 volts is applied, it reads full scale. Now if you break the circuit, as in Fig. 8-1, and insert a resistance (or reactance) in circuit, the reading drops. The meter can be calibrated to read the amount of reactance, or better, calibrated directly in microfarads and micromicrofarads. The easy way is to make up a chart and hang it on the wall near where you keep the meter.

THE CAPACITANCE BRIDGE

By far the most practical device used to measure capacitance is the <u>bridge</u>. It also measures resistance, in most commercial units, and sometimes inductance. The principle of the Wheatstone bridge (which was invented by a man named Christie, by the way) is to balance two sets of resistors exactly. As you can see in Fig. 8-2, current passes through the two

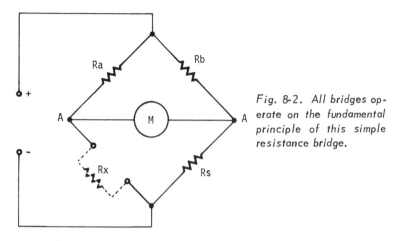

Fig. 8-2. All bridges operate on the fundamental principle of this simple resistance bridge.

pairs of resistors in parallel. If Ra and Rb have the same resistance, and Rs and Rx also have the same resistance, the voltage drop across Ra and Rb will be the same, points AA will have the same voltage, and no current can flow through the meter.

For example, suppose that resistors, Ra, Rb, and Rs are 10 ohms each. We insert an unknown resistor at Rx, and the bridge "balances" (no current flows through the meter). We know that Rx is 10 ohms. But what if we want to test other resistors? Easy! Simply vary one of the "known" arms of the bridge. Suppose Rx were 100 ohms. If we make either Ra or Rs 100 ohms, the voltage at points AA will be identical, and the bridge will balance. (Or we could drop Rb to 1 ohm for the same result, since the ratio of the arms would be the same.) The preferred approach is to vary Rx so the same amount of current flows in each arm. This is the usual approach (the "s" in Rs means "standard"). In practical bridges it will probably be a carefully calibrated variable resistor; in laboratory bridges possibly a decade box of precision resistors.

But why talk about resistors? We want to measure <u>capacitors</u>, you say. Well, most capacitor bridges measure resistors, too, but the real reason is that it's easier to explain a resistor bridge. The capacitor bridge employs the same principle and it is not too much more complex. First, we have to use AC instead of DC; second we have to insert a capacitor instead of a resistor for Rx. (It becomes Cx now.) To measure capacitors of different sizes, we can either vary Cx or a resistor arm. Since resistors are cheaper than capacitors, the practical instrument uses a variable resistor (pot) with a large dial, calibrated in ohms and microfarads.

A practical capacitance-resistance bridge circuit, like that in Fig. 8-3, usually (but not always) combines Ra and Rb in a single pot. As the value of one gets larger the other gets smaller, thus the ratio between the two changes. Rs then need not be variable, and can consist of a number of resistors and capacitors selectable with a range switch. Typical values would be 200 ohms, 20,000 ohms and 2 megohms for the resistor bank, and 200 pfd, .02 mfd, and 2 mfd for the capaci-

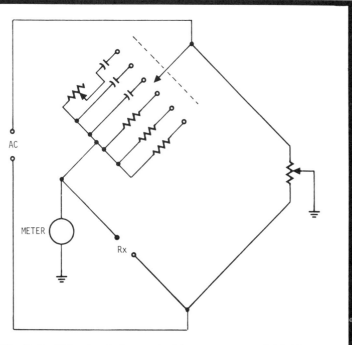

Fig. 8-3. This circuit is standard in most commercial bridges. "Meter" may often be the input to an amplifier or electron-ray tube, or it can even be a pair of headphones. Typical circuit values: Resistors—200 ohms, 2,000 ohms, and 2 megohms. Capacitors—.0002, .02 and 2 mfd. Pots—1,000 ohms.

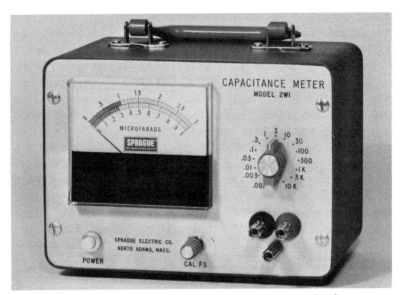

Fig. 8-4. This newer capacitance meter circuit uses AC voltmeter.

tors. This makes it possible to measure a large range of resistors and capacitors.

Old electrolytics develop a certain amount of resistance and the bridge can be balanced perfectly only against a capacitance-resistance combination, so a variable resistor is put in series with the capacitor on the highest capacitance range. When the capacitance and resistance of the arm are equal to that of the capacitor, the bridge balances. Balance is indicated on most bridges with an electron-ray ("magic eye") tube, although the trend to a meter—which can be used for leakage measurement and other purposes—is increasing.

The leakage test consists of applying the full working voltage to the capacitor and checking the leakage, either with an "eye" tube or by direct measurement on a meter. The voltage across the capacitor can be increased in steps to the rated voltage. This technique gives electrolytics a chance to "form" so they will be able to stand full voltage by the time it is applied to them. It is a good idea to test an electrolytic for leakage before checking it for capacitance. A few minutes' application of the working voltage will reduce the power factor of an off-the-shelf capacitor.

Several capacitance testers are shown in Fig. 8-4, 8-6, and 8-7. One of the newer capacitance meter uses the AC voltmeter approach previously mentioned (Fig. 8-1). In the Sprauge 2W1 (Fig. 8-4), an alternating voltage is applied to a resistor and the unknown capacitor in series (Fig. 8-5). Fifteen of these resistors are switched to give the meter 15 ranges, from full scale at 0.01 mfd to 10,000 mfd. The meter reads directly in microfarads, with one scale reading to 1 and the other to 3. For example, if the switch is set at 300 mfd and the pointer indicates 2.5, the capacitance indicated is 250 mfd.

The Sprague TCA-1 shown in Fig. 8-6 is a multi-range capacitance and power bridge, an insulation resistance checker for electrostatic (film, ceramic, etc.) capacitors, and it incorporates a leakage current test for electrolytics. Capacitance measurements from 1 pfd to 2000 mfd are made by using a 5-range line-frequency capacitance bridge circuit. A Wein bridge circuit is used for measuring capacitance and power factor. The bridge circuit is balanced on all ranges by a highly accurate wirewound resistor. The standard capacitors are stablized and in parallel with factory-adjusted trimmers to compensate for variations in wiring capacity. A variable resistor is used to set the sensitivity of the amplifier. When the bridge is balanced, indicating the value of the capacitor being tested, the eye closes. A flickering eye often indicates an intermittent capacitor. And if the eye will not close at all, the capacitor is likely to be open.

Many capacitor checkers offer an in-circuit test (Fig. 8-7) which spots open or shorted capacitors without removing them from circuit. However, capacitors with leakage must be test-

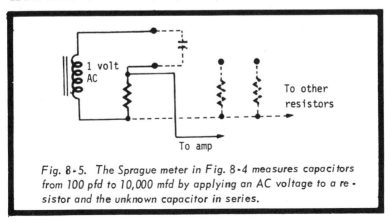

Fig. 8-5. The Sprague meter in Fig. 8-4 measures capacitors from 100 pfd to 10,000 mfd by applying an AC voltage to a resistor and the unknown capacitor in series.

155

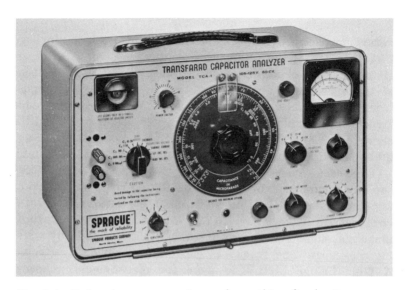

Fig. 8-6. Referred to as a capacitor analyzer, this refined unit measures capacitors from 1 pfd to 2,000 mfd and has many special features designed to improve accuracy, protect low-voltage capacitors, etc.

Fig. 8-7. Later capacitance testers are designed for in-circuit operation as well as normal out-of-circuit tests. This unit also features a low-voltage test for capacitors used in transistorized circuits.

ed out of the circuit. The open test employs an oscillating circuit so adjusted that a capacitive load across the test prods either puts it into oscillation or stops it from oscillating. (Both approaches have been used.) The RF circuit is also used to check for shorts, either by checking the voltage set up across the capacitor or by using a circuit that goes out of oscillation when the impedance drops to a certain point. Since a short or partial short lowers the impedance, this is an effective test.

One word of caution: in-circuit capacitance tests will often be ineffective on small capacitors (less than 25 pfd) or those with shunting resistances less than 50 ohms. In these instances, the capacitors should be checked out of the circuit. Instrument test manuals will normally indicate these values if they apply. The reactance of a .001 capacitor is around 8 ohms at 20 MHz, and that of a .01 capacitor less than 1 ohm. But you are seldom quite sure what is across your capacitor. In one old all-wave radio, for example, an innocent 500-pfd bypass capacitor might turn out to be connected directly across a filter capacitor and electrolytics can have a lot of resistance on the shorter waves. In any case where you are not sure, disconnect one end of the capacitor and check it out-of-circuit.

Some capacitor checkers have other features, including the means for extending the capacitance range to measure very large capacitors, facilities for diode and transistor leakage testing, special low bridge voltages, polarizing voltages for low-voltage polarized capacitors (used in many transistor circuits), and others. Most checkers have connections for an external standard and can be used as inductance bridges by connecting a known inductance to those terminals. Inductances are most difficult to measure. Many of them have high power factors and it may be next to impossible to balance the bridge if the standard and the unknown inductors differ widely in their resistance/reactance ratios.

USING THE CAPACITANCE CHECKER

There are two main types or circuits in which trouble in a capacitor spells trouble in the equipment. One of these is the circuit with high voltage on one side of the capacitor, and on the other side a circuit where current flow is limited by resistors. The other is filter circuits; loss of capacitance in a filter capacitor is one of the most common causes of trouble.

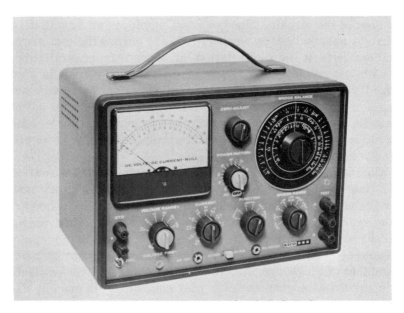

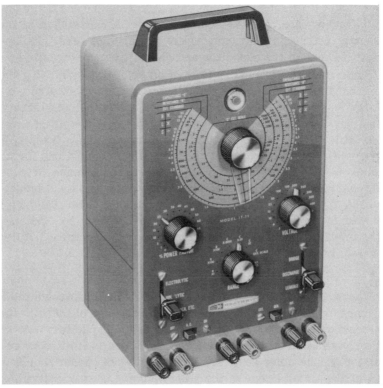

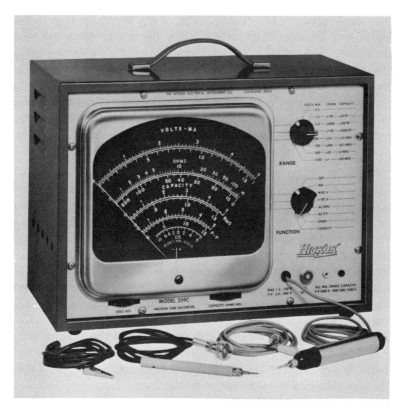

Pictured on these two pages are three useful and relatively inexpensive capacitance measuring instruments. The Eico Model 965 (upper left) uses a meter to show bridge null, as well as indicating leakage directly. It can also be used independently as a VTVM and a VT ammeter; it offers 11 ranges from 15 microamperes to 15 ma. The low bridge voltages and polarizing voltages make it useful for tantalum and other low voltage capacitors. The Heathkit Model IT-11 bridge (bottom left) measures capacitors from 10 pfd to 1,000 mfd, resistors from 5 ohms to 50 megohms, and also has terminals for external standards. Balance is indicated by an eye tube. The 9-inch meter on the Hickok Model 209C (above) VTVM also includes a capacitance scale. The capacitor under test is placed in series with an internal 60-Hz voltage source. The current, which varies the size of the capacitor, is rectified and measured on the meter scale calibrated to read in capacitance. It is designed to measure capacitance from 50 pfd to 2,000 mfd.

In the Mercury 1400 tester, Fig. 8-7, the capacitor tester leads can be placed directly across any electrolytic to check its value. Polarity is not important since this unit and many others like it use a low voltage AC test signal. Multiple-section filter capacitors should be tested one section at a time by connecting one test lead to the common negative and the other to each positive terminal in sequence. If you don't know the value of the capacitor, use the highest range and work down. The higher value units are generally found in radio and TV chassis.

Defective capacitors in automatic gain control (or AVC in sound circuits) are the most noticeable. In some of these we have a fairly large voltage on one side of the capacitor and a circuit containing multi-megohm resistors on the other side. Leakage of a very small current across megohms of resistance can run the voltage up to where you get a white raster with no evidence of a picture. And in sound circuits they can drive the control grid positive and distort the signal beyond recognition. The best approach in this type of circuit is to unsolder the low-circuit end of the capacitor and use the equipment's own voltage to check it. Set the voltmeter on a high enough scale to protect it if the capacitor is completely shorted, then connect the voltmeter between the loose capacitor lead and ground to check for any evidence of leakage.

The most common fault in large capacitors is a loss of capacitance. Leakage is not so important (except as it increases the power factor and reduces their filtering efficiency). The load resistance is across them and a few more milliamperes makes little difference. But a loss of capacitance raises the impedance of the power supply and increases the ripple in the various pulse, video, sweep, and other signals. If it doesn't, singles begin to mix with each other to produce some of the real hard-to-figure-out problems. These are sometimes the one-station, early-evening, and intermittent troubles that don't show up when the equipment is brought in and set up on the bench. In such cases check the power factor of the filter capacitors as well as their capacitance. A high power factor means resistance between B-plus and ground and that resistance means possible unwanted coupling between circuits.

Cathode bypass capacitors may also cause trouble if they lose some of their capacitance. Leakage or power factor in itself

160

means little here, since most cathode bypass capacitors are already shunted by low-value resistors. But a loss of capacitance may allow the cathode resistor to introduce negative feedback, reducing the output. In some transistor circuits you may get the opposite result—positive feedback.

There are some bypass capacitor circuits where a loss of capacitance is much more important than leakage. A screen bypass, for example, can be quite leaky without affecting circuit operation, although in some circuits an open or nearly open screen bypass causes immediate oscillation. Open capacitors in series signal circuits can stop everything, while a loss of capacitance may cause distortion in some pulse or audio circuits.

Wherever you see a capacitor rated at 5% tolerance in a circuit that is giving trouble, it's a good idea to test it. Over-capacitance, though much rarer than loss of capacitance, can also give trouble. If a capacitor is expected to charge up to a certain voltage during one horizontal scan, for instance, and its value is too high, the capacitor may charge up to only half that voltage and change the entire scan rate. It's always a good idea to inspect soldered leads for evidence that a capacitor has been replaced recently if a set has been giving trouble that leads you to suspect capacitors. Replacement is practically the only way you can get into trouble with over-capacitance.

So a capacitance checker can be useful in two ways: as a time saver in cases where you might search for hours to find the trouble if you didn't have it and in quite a few cases where you could never be quite sure till you replaced the capacitor with one known go be good and the right size, and substitution may not always be convenient. A capacitance checker is one of the instruments that "grows" on you. If you have one on your bench you will find yourself using it more and more as you become familiär with it.

CHAPTER 9

Probes

So far, we have failed to pay any attention other than a passing mention to some of our most important pieces of test equipment—the probes that connect instruments to the points in the electronic equipment where we want to measure something or check a component. In the simplest form they consist of a cable (or two wires) with a pair of prods on one end and plugs or a plug at the meter end. The cable may be shielded, with the shield acting as the ground, cold, or return lead of the probe. But by shielding the hot test lead we add capacitance, an effect which can be reduced by inserting a resistor in the "hot" test prod, as in Fig. 9-1.

RESISTANCE PROBE

The resistance-type probe is universal with VTVMs and the resistance in the probe is invariably 1 megohm. On the other hand, a VOM is calibrated for use with a direct probe, simply a piece of shielded wire, as in Fig. 9-2. The direct probe is also very generally used with oscilloscopes.

It is sometimes a good idea to use a resistor probe with a VOM to reduce circuit loading, or in cases where the equipment breaks into oscillation when a direct probe is attached

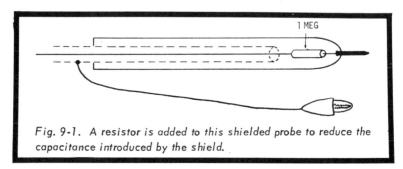

Fig. 9-1. A resistor is added to this shielded probe to reduce the capacitance introduced by the shield.

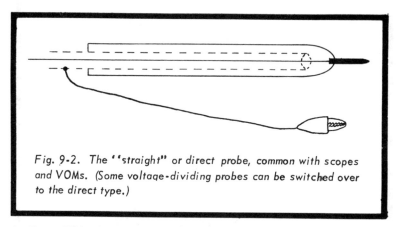

Fig. 9-2. The "straight" or direct probe, common with scopes and VOMs. (Some voltage-dividing probes can be switched over to the direct type.)

to it.   This is essential if the VOM is a low-impedance unit and circuit loading is critical. But remember to allow for the probe resistance when reading the meter. For example, the resistance of a 20,000-thousand ohm-per-volt meter on the 50-volt range is 1 megohm. Putting a 1-megohm resistor in your test probe doubles the resistance exactly and cuts the current through the meter in half. It now takes 100 volts to drive the pointer to full scale, so you have to multiply the readings by 2. On the 500-volt scale the meter's internal resistance would be 10 megohms, so the probe would make it necessary to increase the readings by only 10% to get the true voltage.   The probes in Figs. 9-3 and 9-4 function as either isolating or direct.

THE VOLTAGE-DIVIDING PROBE

Next to the direct probe and the resistance (or isolating) types, the voltage-dividing probe is the most common and most useful. As shown in Fig. 9-5 it consists of two resistors in series, and the input to the instrument is tapped off at their junction. It is used with the scope and, except in audio work, is probably used more than any other scope probe. It's great advantage is that it reduces the capacitive load across the circuit being checked.   The capacitor in the probe is in series with the input capacitance of the scope and cable. The capacitor and resistors are so calculated that nine-tenths of the voltage is across the resistor and capacitor in the probe and only one-tenth across the scope input. Thus the circuit being checked sees only one-tenth the actual input capacitance of

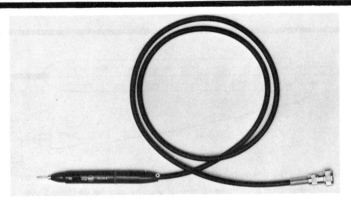

Fig. 9-3. This probe is "switchable"—isolating or direct.

Fig. 9-4. Another switch type: DC or AC/OHMS probe for VTVM.

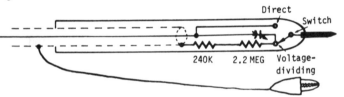

Fig. 9-5. Capacitive and resistive loading are both cut nine-tenths by voltage-dividing probes.

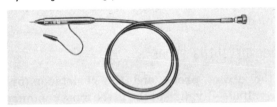

Fig. 9-6. A voltage-dividing probe with a direct position.

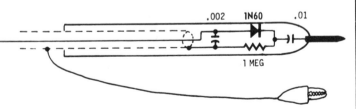

Fig. 9-7. The demodulator probe "detects" RF signals and supplies an audio or video signal.

the scope. The probe in Fig. 9-6 also has a direct position.

The scope's input capacitance may be on the order of 20 pfd and each foot of cable may add as much. This could result in distortion at high frequencies, detune the circuits under test, and help create oscillation. So the low-capacitance probe is preferred for many applications, especially in TV servicing. Of course, you can't expect to get the advantages of the low-capacitance probe for nothing—it cuts the sensitivity of your scope to one-tenth of what it would be with a direct probe A wave that would be 2 1/2 inches high with the direct probe is only 1/2 inch high when you switch in the voltage-dividing one.

The voltage-dividing probe can be used in another way: to measure voltages higher than can be applied direct to most scopes. (Don't carry this too far though; the low-capacitance unit is definitely not a substitute for the more expensive high-voltage probe!) For instance, you can use it to measure the voltage on the deflection coils in a TV circuit, but don't try it on the 4,000-volt pulse from the horizontal output tube. You can get an excellent idea of the waveform and height by holding the test prod close to the tube cap, or clipping it to the outside of the insulation on the lead from the cap.

THE DEMODULATOR PROBE

You often want to know something about the amplitude or form of an RF signal. Here is where the detector or demodulator probe comes in. Used in a video IF circuit, it acts just like the video detector to give you a picture of the waveform on the scope. If you use it in high-level radio IFs, you will be able to hear the signal in a pair of headphones connected across its output. Or you can feed the probe output into an amplifier to hear weaker signals. Used with a VTVM it gives you a rough idea of signal amplitudes at frequencies higher than the VTVMs AC section can handle. The input voltage of a demodulator probe is limited—about 30 volts AC is the maximum.

The demodulator probe shown in Fig. 9-7 consists of a crystal (diode) detector, a capacitor to block DC, and a resistor to complete the diode DC circuit. Since it has capacitance and resistance, it may load an IF and cause it to oscillate. If this happens, move the probe to different test points. Notice that a demodulator probe is just the opposite to a low-capacitance probe. Its impedance is lower and its capacitance higher than that of the usual isolation probe and it can distort high-frequency signals. But it does tell you whether a signal is there or not, and it gives you a fair idea of its amplitude. In low-impedance circuits it's fine; just be careful of using it in places where a low-capacitance probe is recommended. They

Fig. 9-8. Demodulator probes. "A" is for a VTVM and "B" is a slip-on type to go over a direct probe.

usually have good sensitivity and because of this they can distort the video signal. Two typical demodulator probes are pictured in Fig. 9-8.

THE HIGH-VOLTAGE PROBE

We have long had circuits with voltages far higher than our ordinary service instruments can handle—the high voltage on the TV kinescope ultor, for example. But in most cases we have been content to use rough tests to assure ourselves that the voltage was there and not far from correct, rather than purchase and use a high-voltage probe. Now, color TV has changed all that. The manual instructs you to <u>measure</u> the high voltage and even gives voltage tolerances on the regulator tube. Present restrictions on X-rays emitted from that tube makes it advisable to keep within those tolerances. It may help your personal health, too. You—not the viewer— are the person who is likely to be within five centimeters of the equipment for long periods of time.

The differences between the high-voltage (Fig. 9-9) and the ordinary isolating probe are in the size of the probe resistor, which may be 1,000 megohms instead of 1 megohm, and in the insulation, which is designed to protect the careful operator working with voltages up to 25,000 or more. Therefore, you would expect to use it like a VTVM isolating probe with the higher multiplication factor, and you must use it 100 times as carefully! At 25,000 volts you are dealing with a low-potential form of lightning. Such voltages sometimes look on ordinary insulation as a fair conductor and on the technician as a rather good ground! The one-hand rule applies to all high-voltage work—keep the other in your pocket. If you must work on a concrete floor in a basement, put down a heavy rubber mat. (This is a good rule for work with all but transistor voltages.)

The safest way to measure high voltage is to hook up the ground connection with the power off. Then turn on the juice, approach the equipment with arm extended, contact the terminal, take your measurement, and turn the equipment off again. "Prodding around" is the ideal way to get into real trouble. The high-voltage probe, even with its 100-to-1 reduction, often gives more accurate results in high-impedance, moderately high-voltage circuits than the lower impedance 10-to-1 voltage-dividing probe. Since it usually runs 1,000 meghoms to the 10 meghoms of the ordinary VTVM, it cannot be used for low voltages. (All scales on the meter must be multiplied by 100)

A voltage-dividing high-voltage probe (Fig. 9-10) is also de-

Fig. 9-9. High-voltage probe, designed to protect the user.

Fig. 9-10. Capacitance-type voltage divider probe; it is also a slip-on.

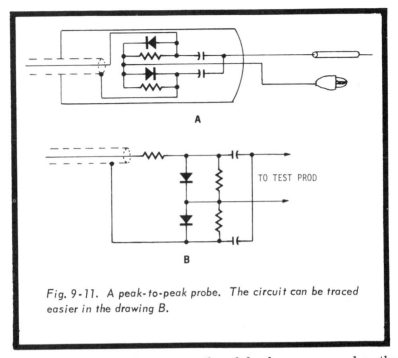

Fig. 9-11. A peak-to-peak probe. The circuit can be traced easier in the drawing B.

scribed in service literature, though few have appeared on the commercial market. It consists of two capacitors in series, like the two resistors in Fig. 9-5. Home constructors have been instructed to build such a probe with a 1X2A high-voltage rectifier tube as a vacuum capacitor for the high-voltage section. The other capacitor, across which the instrument is connected, is a trimmer. It is adjusted so that the meter scale reads one hundredth of the actual voltage. One capacitance-type voltage-dividing probe, marketed commercially, obviously uses a much more compact type of high-voltage capacitor than the 1 X 2-A, but it is limited to about 5,000 volts.

SPECIAL PROBES

Peak-to-peak probes are often mentioned, and can be obtained commercially. This probe is a voltage doubler with which you can read peak-to-peak voltages on a DC VTVM. One precaution is necessary: no ground other than the cable of the voltmeter and the ground lead of the probe may be used. Fig. 9-11B shows that connecting a "grounding" lead between the VTVM and the equipment being tested would short out the lower part of the voltage-doubling circuit.

The chromatic probe should probably be classed as a "diode mixer" rather than a probe. With it you can produce a swept signal wide enough and flat enough to check color video circuits accurately. It consists simply of three diodes in parallel (to reduce impedance). The combined output of an AM and a swept signal generator is applied to the input (Fig. 9-12) and the output is a video signal with bandwidth equal to the difference in frequency between the two generators.

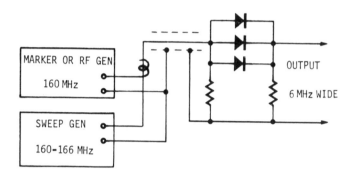

Fig. 9-12. The chroma probe is a modulator that combines two frequencies to obtain a third one.

The <u>electrostatic pickup</u> probe is well known, though not under a formal name. It is the type you use when you clip the scope lead to an ungrounded tube shield. Waveforms are occasionally checked by bringing the test probe up close to the voltage source. Special ring-shaped probes designed to be placed over tubes have also appeared from time to time as parts of special instruments. One analyzer brought out a few years ago by Kingston Electronics depended on a number of specially-shaped (ring, part ring, etc.) probes to pick up information from above the chassis of a TV set.

Hum (or inductive) probes are also mostly seen with specialized instruments. They consist of a loop of one, several, or many turns of wire, with one end attached to the center conductor of the probe cable and the other to the shield. The true hum pickup probe should be made with many turns of fine wire. It is a useful instrument for finding hum spots on an amplifier chassis.

CHAPTER 10

Tube, Transistor
& Special-Purpose Checkers

There are two schools of thought on tube checking. One points out that tubes can test GOOD on a checker and fail to work under actual conditions in some circuits. Substitution with known-good tubes, they say, is the only true form of tube checking. And, since the advent of television and the necessity of carrying a caddy of spare tubes, the latter school has become more popular today than it was in the past. But, in spite of that, a tube checker has real advantages, says my school. Even if a set has well-defined trouble in, say, the video IF, chances are excellent that some tubes in other portions of the circuit are not in the best of condition. If they are really down, they should be replaced; if they are a little low and the reduced-heater-voltage test shows a decided drop, the customer can be informed and replacement suggested.

If the symptoms do not point immediately to the source of trouble, testing all the tubes in the set may localize it. If they all check GOOD, one possible cause of trouble has been (almost) eliminated. One technician of my acquaintance always tests the tubes in a set as his first operation. It clears the way for further work and often spots the trouble, he says. And besides, he more than pays for his time in the sale of tubes he would otherwise have left in the set. Yet tubes can check GOOD in some types of testers and fail to work in the set. Oscillator circuits tend to be critical in this respect. And some circuits call for short bursts of very high current, an operating condition that the tube tester is not set up to duplicate. But some testers can probe more deeply into tube characteristics than other.

TUBE TESTERS

The most widely used is the _emission_ tester (Fig. 10-1). It is less expensive than mutual conductance types, but a little

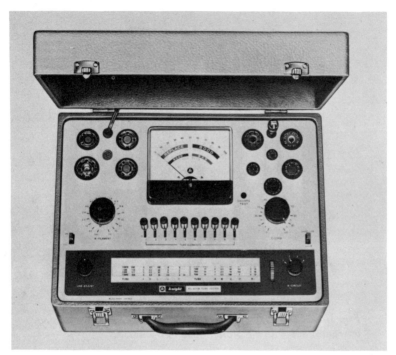

Fig. 10-1. An emission tester of this type also checks for shorts.
It may also have an adapter for checking picture tubes. This one
also tests pilot lamps.

limited in its capabilities. It can tell whether a tube is "worn
out" or not, and whether any of its elements are shorted. If
a tube shows up well on regular heater voltage and drops sharply at reduced heater voltage, you can be sure it is on the way
toward failure. These three capabilities enable the emission
tester to handle 99% of the tubes you will have to check.

The mutal conductance tester and its variations dig a little
deeper into tube operating characteristics. Its basic principle
is to apply normal or near-normal voltages to the elements,
then vary the grid voltage and notice the effect on plate current. For example, the tester might be adjusted so the tube
would show zero on the meter with minus 3 volts on the grid.
Pushing the "test" button would bring the grid voltage up to
zero volts, and—for a good tube—the meter indicator would
swing up into the GOOD part of the scale.

Only the more expensive laboratory-type testers follow the
basic principles exactly; in practical mutual conductance test-

171

Fig. 10-2. The CRT checker tests and rejuvenates, performing all operations with the picture tube in the set.

ers the elements may not always receive their exact working voltages, rectifiers may not always be tested at full output, and the grid swing may not be exactly what it would be with a signal in the equipment. However, many of the new tube testers now combine full emission tests, leakage tests, and dynamic conductance. The aim has been to produce a good tester at a price the technician can pay, and many attempts have been remarkably successful.

Dynamic mutual conductance is a term originally applied to a test in which the voltage applied to the grid is AC instead of DC. This type of test more closely approximates actual tube operation in the set. There has been some confusion over the term: One manufacturer refers to dynamic conductance as "combined plate conductance, mutual conductance, and emission" while another speaks of "true mutual conductance using 5,000-Hz square waves."

CRT Tube Tester-Rejuvenators

Many tube testers also supply a socket or adapters for checking CRTS (cathode ray tubes). These instruments normally perform the same functions as a regular tube tester; that is, emission, leakage, and short checks.

Color picture tubes are normally checked the same as B/W types, except that there is more warmup time and balance to consider. The tester in Fig. 10-2 reads the emission of the three color guns. If you take emission readings after two or three minutes and again at five minutes, you can determine whether certain guns have lowered emission and rejuvenate them if desired. Many tube testers have rejuvenators built-in for this purpose. Follow the instrument instructions when rejuvenating or you may end up buying a new tube.

TRANSISTOR TESTERS

The arguments for and against the tube tester are also heard in transistor testing discussions. However, there is one

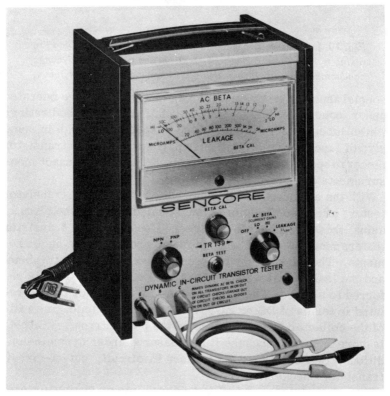

Fig. 10-3. An in-circuit, out-of-circuit transistor tester.

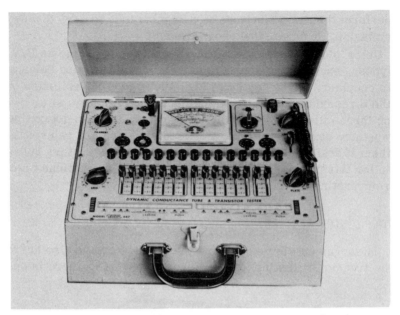

Fig. 10-4. This is both a tube and transistor tester, combined in a single instrument. The tube tester uses a modified dynamic conductance test in which grid voltage is varied for different tubes.

special aspect in testing transistors—transistors are operated under conditions which vary in relation to published ratings while tubes generally run close to specs, although in some circuit functions it may well be important to have the transistor closer to specs than in other circuits. Therefore, exact measurements are preferable.

With the advent of new devices such as the FET, transistor testers are becoming more sophisticated, as are the circuits using these solid-state devices. Consequently, transistor testers must be more accurate and provide more measurements. The most important transistor checks are gain (beta) and the leakage between the base and collector. This is referred to as Icbo. The gain or beta of a transistor can be related in terms of DC or AC. DC beta is called hfe, the ratio of the collector circuit divided by the base current. AC beta is more important because it is measured under dynamic conditions. Fig. 10-3 shows a modern in-circuit, out-of-circuit transistor checker.

Since transistors are often soldered into an equipment circuit board, most checkers are designed to test transistors "in-circuit." The method used is to apply an AC voltage to the transistor and measure the AC gain or beta. This test, quite correctly, is also referred to as a "dynamic test." The out-of-circuit transistor tests measure gain (beta) and leakage between elements. The FET or MOSFET is usually tested in somewhat the same way. An AC signal is applied between the "source" and "gate" and the amplified signal between the "source" and "drain" is measured as mutual conductance. Because circuit components can also be defective, if you are in doubt when making in-circuit transistor tests, remove the unit and re-test it. Most transistor testers also check diodes. A special SCR Analyzer is used for silicon controlled rectifiers.

TRANSISTOR-TUBE TESTERS

A transistor and tube tester are often combined into one instrument (Fig. 10-4), and in some cases the transistor tester is part of a combination instrument, or analyst, which can be a pretty complete portable radio shop. One such analyst (Fig. 10-5) contains a power supply for auto and transistor radios, a VOM, transistor tester (for in- and out-of-circuit), a signal generator that produces modulated and unmodulated AM

Fig. 10-5. The Radio Analyst offers a near-complete setup for servicing auto, transistor, and other radios.

175

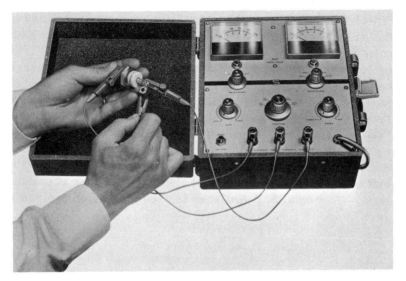

Fig. 10-6. The technician using the SCR checker will have some new experiences: he'll find himself checking peak forward, peak reverse, and gate voltages.

signals over the standard radio broadcast band, shortwave and IF ranges, and an FM signal for the FM band, as well as a front-panel 400-Hz signal for audio tests. Fig. 10-6 shows a silicon controlled rectifier (SCR) tester.

CITIZENS BAND TEST INSTRUMENTS

Since citizens band equipment includes transmitters, it requires a few special instruments to check transmitter operation. One such instrument is a "Transmitter Tester" (Fig. 10-7) which checks power outout and modulation percentage, and it is also a relative field-strength meter. Another instrument, designed for antenna checks (Fig. 10-8), measures standing-wave ratios and power input to the antenna.

Note well that—contrary to many people's ideas—anyone may legally make tests and measurements on CB equipment, but that only a licensed radio operator makes any adjustments that might affect the output power or frequency. Thus, you might find the standing-wave ratio on an antenna to be too high, or the power too low. But you cannot legally make any attempt to improve either unless you are properly licensed and have not only the necessary know-how but the equipment to measure

Fig. 10-7. The "Transmitter Tester" measures RF wattage and modulation percentage. External terminals make it possible to use the 0-1 ma meter independently.

Fig. 10-8. The "Antenna Tester" is a standing-wave ratio meter that can also be used to indicate power output.

Fig. 10-9. This instrument checks the quality of CB crystals and has a number of other specialized CB uses.

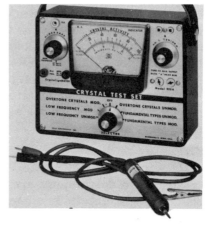

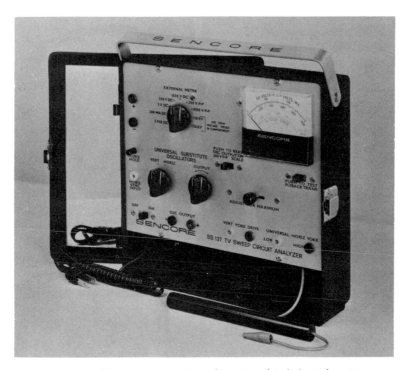

Fig. 10-10. The sweep circuit analyzer is a big help in locating horizontal or vertical sweep or yoke troubles.

your results so you can certify the equipment to be working within legal tolerances.

A crystal test set (Fig. 10-9) which checks the activity and quality—but not the exact frequency—of CB crystals is also available. In the low-frequency position it tests broadcast IF crystals (range 400 to 500 kHz) and the instrument has several subsidiary uses. It can be used as a low-power signal source on small transmitters, an RF power indicator, plate milli-ammeter, and an RF voltmeter. It might well be a useful instrument to the technician already well equipped with instruments but who finds that his equipment falls a little short for doing work on CB radios.

SWEEP CIRCUIT TESTERS

A number of instruments are made to check single components or single circuits in a more complex array. The sweep circuit analyzer (Fig. 10-10), for example, checks that portion of a TV receiver. It supplies horizontal and vertical sweep signals to check the corresponding oscillators by signal substitution; a substitute universal horizontal yoke that is used to show up any defect in the set's own yoke; and a flyback tester. An adapter is used to check horizontal output tube cathode current. The meter in the instrument can also be used as a straight VTVM, reading AC and DC to 1,000 volts with a special probe to measure ultor voltages at 10 and 30 KV. (Measurements of horizontal output tube current and screen voltage are made internally, without probes, by pushbutton.)

CATHODE CURRENT CHECKER

One piece of equipment is designed exclusively to measure

Fig. 10-11. Field strength meters are important instruments to television installers in critical areas and especially to cable system designers. For two-way communications, where often only one frequency is checked, simpler instruments may be used.

Fig. 10-12. A truly fundamental instrument, the power line monitor assures the technician that his line voltage is right, or warns him that he may be seeing effects of high or low line voltages in addition to the defects in the equipment he is servicing.

horizontal output tube cathode current. It consists of a number of adapters nested on a case with the tube types for which each is used printed under it, as well as the best rated cathode current for each type. The manual shows several ways the tube can be brought to the best operating condition and recommends adjusting the horizontal linearity coil to attain the lowest cathode current for optimum operation. This operation, the manual says, it particularly valuable in color tube circuitry as it prolongs convergence quality and improves focus.

FIELD STRENGTH METERS

A field-strength meter is actually a specially designed, sensitive receiver with a microammeter to indicate the relative strength of a received signal (Fig. 10-11). The meter, depending upon its tuning range, has unlimited uses in radio,

TV, and FM communications. For example, it can be tuned to a TV channel and will indicate the relative strenght of a signal at that location. It also is helpful in orienting an antenna (FM or TV) in any desired direction. With the field-strength meter tuned to receive the signal the antenna can be rotated until the meter indicates maximum. This technique is especially useful for technicians working on master TV antenna systems (MATV). Also, knowing the signal strength of various TV signals to be carried on an MATV system, it is easy to determine the amount of amplification required to distribute the proper signal level to all sets in the system. In some locations, a local TV signal may need to be attenuated or reduced, while at the same time a weaker signal must be amplified.

We will not go into the numerous service aids such as capacitor and resistor decades. They are mounted in instrument-like boxes, and while very useful tools they are actually extensions of the "substitute a known-good one" approach rather than instruments. In conclusion, it seems appropriate to introduce an instrument useful to any technician or experimenter—a line voltage monitor (Fig. 10-12). Quite often an inoperative circuit—especially an oscillator—is the consequence of low line voltage.

CHAPTER 11

Signal Tracing Instruments

As pointed out in preceding chapters, several types of test instruments are used in circuit signal tracing and troubleshooting—RF signal generators, audio generators, sweep-marker generators, and oscilloscopes or oscilloscope/vectorscope combinations. Let's look a little closer at some of these units and their applications.

RF SIGNAL GENERATORS

An RF signal generator such as shown in Fig. 11-1 provides output frequencies from 100 kHz to 54 MHz. It can be used as an alignment instrument or for signal injection during troubleshooting procedures. It also provides a calibrated output level which can be modulated either from its own internal 400-Hz audio oscillator or from an external

Fig. 11-1. The Knight KG-686 RF signal generator covers 100 kHz to 54 MHz and has a calibrated output. (Courtesy Allied Radio)

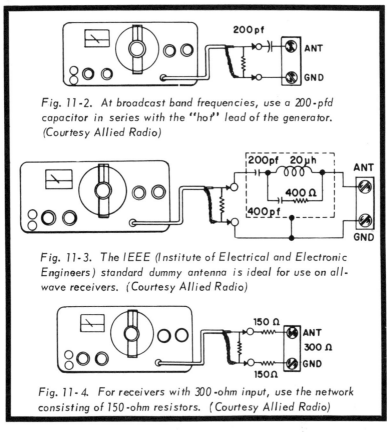

Fig. 11-2. At broadcast band frequencies, use a 200-pfd capacitor in series with the "hot" lead of the generator. (Courtesy Allied Radio)

Fig. 11-3. The IEEE (Institute of Electrical and Electronic Engineers) standard dummy antenna is ideal for use on all-wave receivers. (Courtesy Allied Radio)

Fig. 11-4. For receivers with 300-ohm input, use the network consisting of 150-ohm resistors. (Courtesy Allied Radio)

modulation source. The generator in Fig. 11-1 has a 50-ohm output. The diagrams in Figs. 11-2, 11-3 and 11-4 show the various matching networks used between the generator and receiver for making receiver sensitivity measurements when the receiver input impedance does not match the output of the generator. When using a generator of this type for alignment or signal injection, a DC-blocking capacitor of .01 to .1-mfd should be used to protect the attenuator resistors from damage by the operating voltages in the receiver being tested.

AM BROADCAST RECEIVER ALIGNMENT

When using an RF signal generator for alignment, always keep the ground lead as close to the signal input as possible and use the cable supplied by the manufacturer, as it is de-

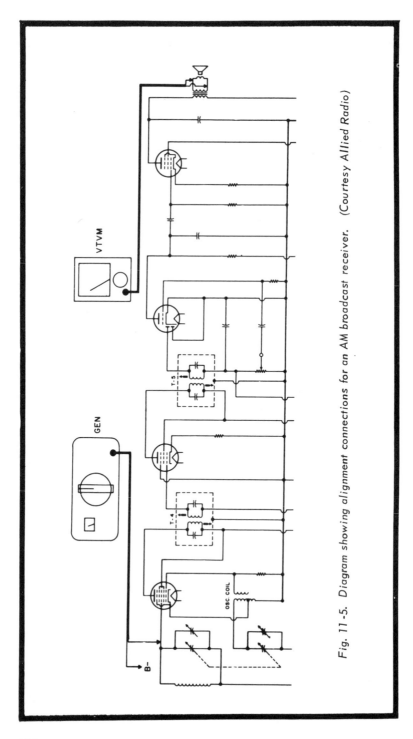

Fig. 11-5. Diagram showing alignment connections for an AM broadcast receiver. (Courtesy Allied Radio)

signed to match the generator output. Anytime you are working in a receiver which has no power transformer (a so-called AC-DC type), its a good idea to use an isolation transformer. The diagram in Fig. 11-5 shows the use of the RF signal generator for aligning a typical AM broadcast receiver.

Usually the receiver manufacturer recommends disabling the local oscillator. In the receiver shown in Fig. 11-5, this can be done by putting a "jumper" wire across the oscillator coil. Then disconnect the speaker and connect an AC VTVM across the transformer voice coil leads. The speaker can be used as an output indicator if an AC VTVM is not used, but tuning the receiver by "ear" will not be as accurate. Set the AC VTVM on a low AC range and connect the generator RF output lead to the grid of the mixer through a .02-mfd capacitor. Set the generator for an output at 455 kHz at 30% modulation. Adjust the receiver volume to a normal listening level and set the generator output attenuators to give you an indication on the AC VTVM. Manufacturers usually specify how much signal should be used, and the generator output level may have to be reduced as the receiver is aligned to keep the signal input low. The IF transformer should be tuned for maximum output on the AC VTVM (or for maximum audio at the speaker) by tuning the secondary, then primary of each transformer, starting with the last one and moving toward the front end. Then go back and "touch" them all up for maximum. Be sure to keep the generator level low.

Remove the oscillator shorting wire and connect the generator to the receiver antenna terminals. Set the generator to 600 kHz and adjust the oscillator trimmer for maximum output. Set the generator to 1500 kHz and adjust the RF trimmer for maximum output.

The RF generator can also be used to align the 10.7-MHz IF and ratio detector stages in an FM receiver as shown in Fig. 11-6. In this case, the generator is connected according to the manufacturer's instructions which may indicate that you connect it to the antenna or through a 10-pfd capacitor to the FM mixer grid. A VTVM is connected to the point specified as shown and the local oscillator is disabled as in the AM receiver. Set the generator for an unmodulated output at 10.7 MHz at the proper output level for the manufacturer's

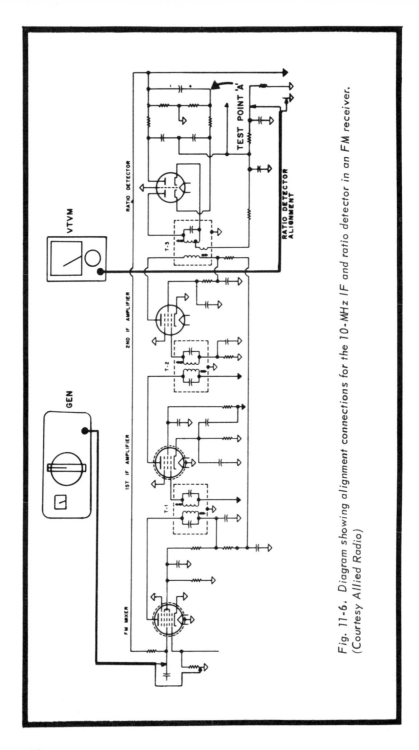

Fig. 11-6. Diagram showing alignment connections for the 10-MHz IF and ratio detector in an FM receiver. (Courtesy Allied Radio)

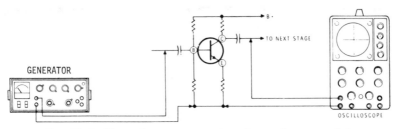

Fig. 11-7. Typical setup connections for testing a transistor amplifier stage. (Courtesy Heath Co.)

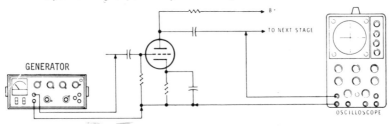

Fig. 11-8. Typical setup connections for testing tube-type amplifier stage. (Courtesy Heath Co.)

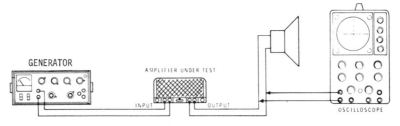

Fig. 11-9. Typical test setup using a sine-or square-wave input. (Courtesy Heath Co.)

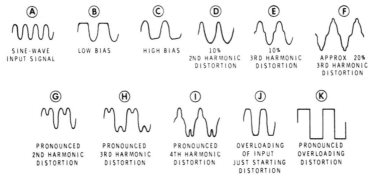

Fig. 11-10. Waveforms B through K show typical distortion patterns with a normal sine-wave input as in A. (Courtesy Heath Co.)

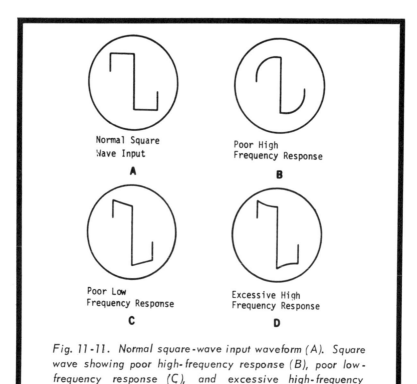

Normal Square
Wave Input

A

Poor High
Frequency Response

B

Poor Low
Frequency Response

C

Excessive High
Frequency Response

D

Fig. 11-11. Normal square-wave input waveform (A). Square wave showing poor high-frequency response (B), poor low-frequency response (C), and excessive high-frequency response (D).

specified meter reading. Then adjust the primary and secondary coils of T1, T2, and the primary of T3. Disconnect the VTVM and adjust it for a center (zero) scale reading, then connect it to the detector output or the test point specified by the manufacturer. Tune the secondary of T3 to obtain a center (zero) reading.

AUDIO GENERATORS

The audio generators discussed in Chapter 7 can be used for testing hi-fi amplifiers, for frequency measurements, pulse measurements, and as an external audio source for an RF generator. The diagrams in Fig. 11-7, 11-8, and 11-9 show several audio amplifier test setups using the sine wave from the generator and an oscilloscope. The waveforms in Fig. 11-10 show typical patterns obtained during these tests and some types of distortion.

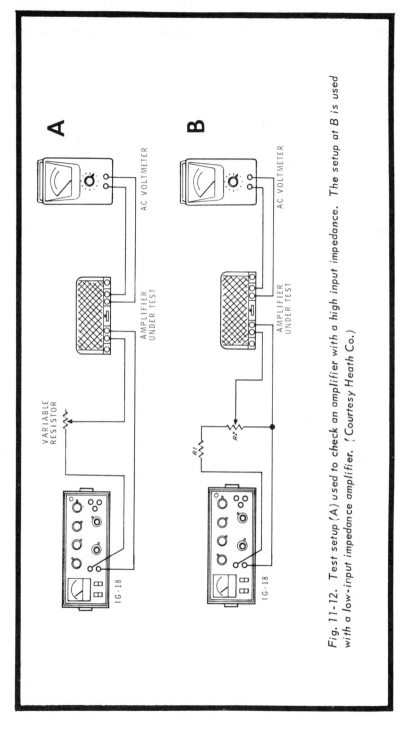

Fig. 11-12. Test setup (A) used to check an amplifier with a high input impedance. The setup at B is used with a low-input impedance amplifier. (Courtesy Heath Co.)

A

B

AC VOLTMETER

AMPLIFIER UNDER TEST

VARIABLE RESISTOR

IG-18

AC VOLTMETER

AMPLIFIER UNDER TEST

R1

R2

IG-18

189

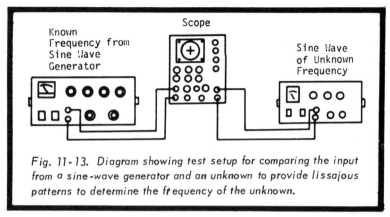

Fig. 11-13. Diagram showing test setup for comparing the input from a sine-wave generator and an unknown to provide lissajous patterns to determine the frequency of the unknown.

The square-wave output from the audio generator is also used for testing amplifiers because a square wave is actually a very complex waveform. It is made up of many sine waves including the fundamental frequency and all the odd harmonics of that frequency. So by testing an amplifier with a square wave, we actually detemine its response to many frequencies at the same time. The test setups are the same as for a sine wave (Fig. 11-7, 11-8, and 11-9); various response waveforms are shown in Fig. 11-11A, B, C, and D.

IMPEDANCE MEASUREMENTS

The diagrams in Fig. 11-12A and 11-12B show how to use the audio generator with an AC voltmeter to measure impedance. The method is exact if the impedance is resistive and approximate if the impedance is reactive. The diagram in Fig. 11-12A is used when measuring input impedances higher than the generator output impedance. With this arrangement, it may be necessary to use several variable resistors of different values such as 10K, 100K, 1 meg and 5 meg to get the correct reading on the AC meter. To use the setup shown in Fig 11-12A, set the generator to a low frequency such as 20 Hz and short out the variable resistor. Set the output level of the generator to give some convenient reading on the AC voltmeter then remove the short from the resistor. Now adjust the resistor until the AC voltmeter reading drops to one-half of the previously set reading. Now all you have to do is take an ohmmeter and read the resistance of the variable resistor and that's your input impedance. This same check at higher frequencies might make the input impedance look smaller because some of the signal would be shorted cut by the input capacitance of the amplifier.

To make low input impedance measurements (a few hundred ohms) use the diagram in Fig. 11-12B. The fixed resistor labeled R1 should be at least 10 times the input impedance to be measured. The value of R1 is not important if it's big enough. The output of the generator is now set to give a convenient reading on the AC voltmeter as before, with R2 shorted out. Then adjust R2 for one-half the previous reading and R2 will equal the input resistance of the amplifier.

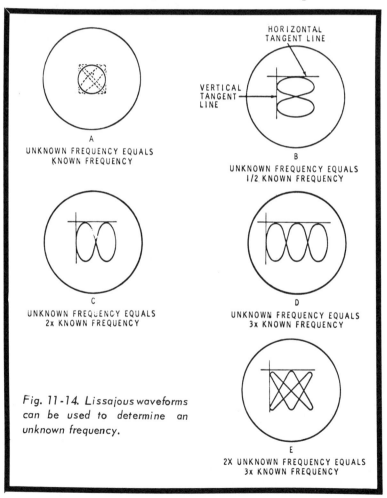

A
UNKNOWN FREQUENCY EQUALS
KNOWN FREQUENCY

HORIZONTAL
TANGENT LINE

VERTICAL
TANGENT
LINE

B
UNKNOWN FREQUENCY EQUALS
1/2 KNOWN FREQUENCY

C
UNKNOWN FREQUENCY EQUALS
2x KNOWN FREQUENCY

D
UNKNOWN FREQUENCY EQUALS
3x KNOWN FREQUENCY

Fig. 11-14. Lissajous waveforms can be used to determine an unknown frequency.

E
2X UNKNOWN FREQUENCY EQUALS
3x KNOWN FREQUENCY

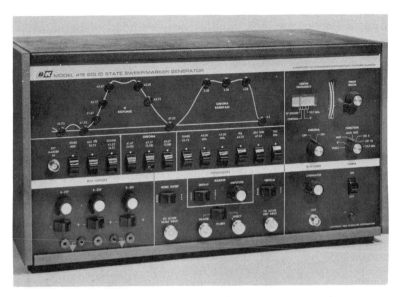

B & K Model 415 solid-state sweep/marker generator, providing preset markers for video IF, chroma, and sound alignment, plus FM IFs.

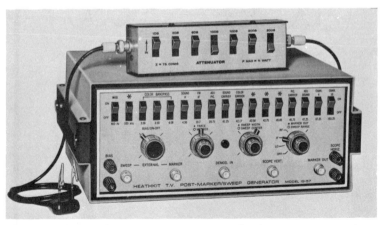

The Heathkit Model IG-57 post-injection marker/sweep generator also offers preset marker frequencies.

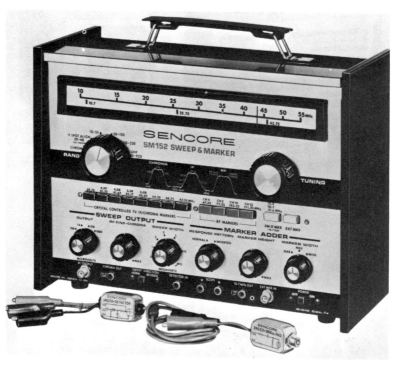

The Sencore SM152 sweep/marker provides variable as well as preset frequencies.

Heathkit Model IG-18 sine/square-wave audio generator.

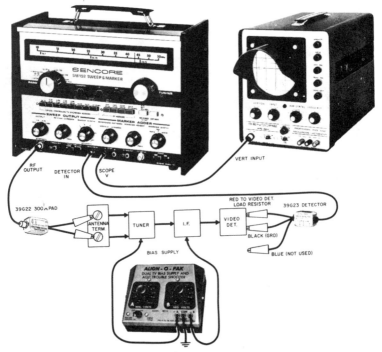

Fig. 11-15. The Sencore SM152 sweep/marker generator showing connections for checking the overall alignment of a TV receiver. (Courtesy Sencore)

FREQUENCY MEASUREMENTS

An oscilloscope and audio generator can be used to measure the frequency of an unknown signal with the arrangement shown in Fig. 11-13. The sine wave from the generator is fed to the scope's horizontal input and the unknown signal to the scope's vertical input terminals. The scope's horizontal frequency selector is set to the horizontal input position.

This procedure simply uses lissajous patterns to compare a known signal (sine-wave generator) with an unknown input. The various lissajous patterns shown in Fig. 11-14 can be used to show the frequency of the unknown by using the equations indicated. To measure an unknown frequency adjust the generator frequency until the pattern comes as close as you can adjust it to the circle shown at A in Fig. 11-14. The circle may appear to revolve in such a way that it alternately assumes each of the following forms: a slanting line to the left, and ellipse, a circle, an ellipse again, a slanting line to the right, an ellipse, etc. Often, it will be almost impossible to keep the circle from revolving.

When the circle is displayed on the oscilloscope screen, the frequency of the unknown signal is then exactly equal to the frequency of the generator and can be read from the generator dial. The accuracy of the measurement is the same as the accuracy of the generator frequency. Unknown frequencies that are beyond the frequency limits of the generator can be measured by using more complex lissajous patterns, such as the ones shown in B, C, D, and E, Fig. 11-14. In these cases, the pattern shown on the oscilloscope gives the ratio between the frequency of the generator signal and the frequency of the unknown signal. Determining the frequency of the unknown signal then becomes a matter of simple arithmetic. The frequency of the unknown signal can be calculated using the following equation:

$$\text{Unknown Frequency} = \frac{T_h \text{ X } F}{T_v}$$

where T_h is the number of loops that touch the horizontal tangent line; F is the generator frequency; and T_v is the number of loops which touch the vertical tangent line.

SWEEP AND MARKER GENERATORS

The sweep/marker generator is one of the most popular of test instruments used today for TV alignment. Some of

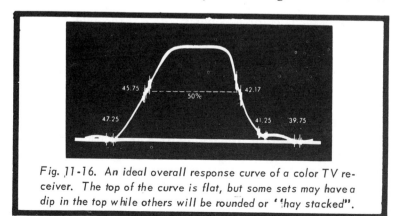

Fig. 11-16. An ideal overall response curve of a color TV receiver. The top of the curve is flat, but some sets may have a dip in the top while others will be rounded or ' 'hay stacked'".

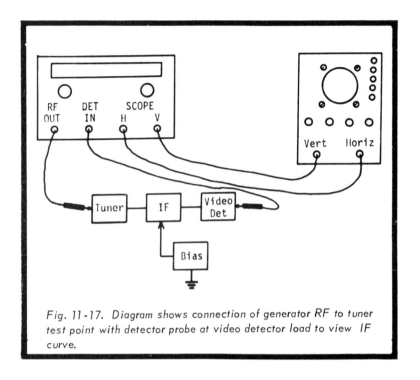

Fig. 11-17. Diagram shows connection of generator RF to tuner test point with detector probe at video detector load to view IF curve.

these units are shown in Chapter 6. The diagram in Fig. 11-15 shows the Sencore SM 152 used to check the overall alignment of a television receiver. An ideal overall response curve of a color receiver is shown in Fig. 11-16. If the waveform indicates that IF alignment is needed, the receiver manufacturer's service instructions should be followed. However, if no information is available, Sencore indicates the following procedures for their SM 152 which can be used on many color receivers with a three-tube IF system. The procedure will not work for transistorized sets; only the manufacturer's directions should be used.

Connect the RF cable with the matching pad to the timer test point or capacity couple the generator to the mixer grid. Set the generator for an output at about 43 MHz and connect the red lead of the detector probe to the video detector load or the grid of the first video amplifier as shown in Fig. 11-17. Then connect the generator to the scope's vertical and horizontal inputs. Connect a bias supply to the AGC test point; set to 2 or 3 volts negative. If you are not sure of the location of the ACG point, connect the bias to the bottom of the grid load resistor on the first IF amplifier. Disable the tuner on VHF by setting it to UHF or set it between channels. Now adjust the sweep/marker generator for a two-volt peak-to-peak response curve on the scope. You should have already calibrated the scope and checked its operation. By looking at the waveform and comparing it with Fig. 11-16, you can now inject the markers from the generator and if they fall where they are supposed to, all is fine. If not, the various traps must be adjusted. The chart in Fig. 11-18 shows the various frequencies controlled by IF transformers in a three-stage color receiver IF.

OSCILLOSCOPE APPLICATIONS

A wideband oscilloscope as shown in Fig. 11-19 or the diagnostic type in Fig. 11-20 are invaluable in almost all types of servicing, particularly in color television. The waveforms in a color receiver are similar to those in a B/W receiver except in the color circuits, of course. Basically, there are four types of waveforms in color receivers with high peak-to-peak triggering pulses. These are the color signals, and the color burst itself.

The color burst can be viewed by connecting the scope to the output of the video detector. The best way to see this is by injecting a color-bar signal into the receiver. You can check color burst from a TV station, but it is often difficult to see the nine cycles of color burst.

An oscilloscope's most important job is to measure peak-to-peak voltages of non-sinusoidal signals as found in TV receivers. When measuring any waveform the scope should be calibrated according to the manufacturer's specifications

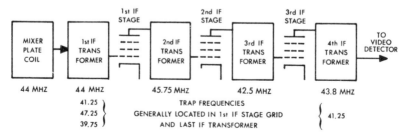

Fig. 11-18. Chart shows the frequencies controlled by the IF transformers in a three-stage IF color receiver. (Courtesy Sencore, Inc.)

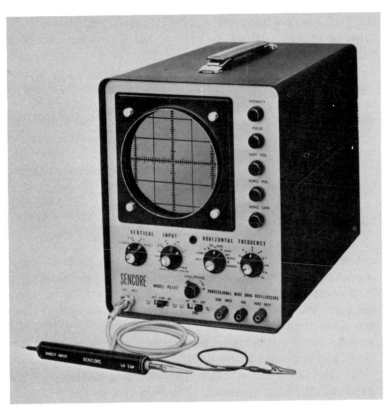

Fig. 11-19. The Sencore Model PS 127 5-inch wideband oscilloscope. (Courtesy Sencore, Inc.)

and the proper probes should be used. There are three probes used with an oscilloscope: direct, low-capacity and demodulator. The direct probe and low-capacity probe are used in audio, video, vertical sync, horizontal sync, color oscillator, color burst, and horizontal oscillator circuits. The reason for the demodulator probe is that it extends the frequency range of the scope input so we can measure signals beyond the passband of the scope.

Another very useful instrument, especially for color demodulator servicing, is the vectorscope. This instrument provides a graphical pattern of the voltages in a demodulator. This type of pattern can be used to adjust the demodulators by connecting a color-bar generator to the TV receiver and adjusting it for a normal color-bar pattern. Then connect the vectorscope leads to the red, blue, and green grids of the picture tube (check the manufacturer's instructions for proper operation and setup). The patterns may vary between TV receivers as some use 90° demodulator systems and others use 105° systems. The two patterns are shown in Figs. 11-21 and 11-22. If the pattern "arms" can be lined up with the proper marks for the R-Y, B-Y, and the 10th bar in the proper amplitudes using the receiver tint control, all is well in the demodulators. If one of the colors is weak, the amplitude will be less than normal. If the R-Y arm does not line up properly by rotating the receiver tint

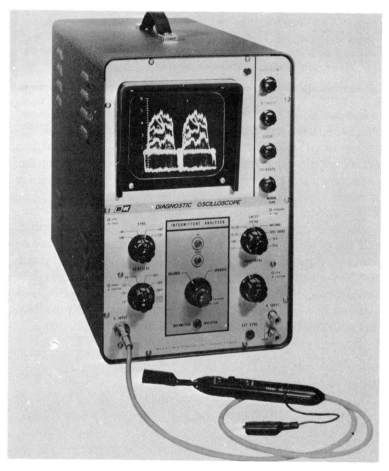

Fig. 11-20. B & K diagnostic oscilloscope Model 1450 is a combination oscilloscope/vectorscope and features provision for an intermittent monitor. (Courtesy B & K, Dynascan Div.)

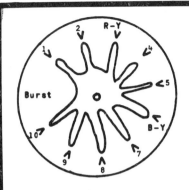

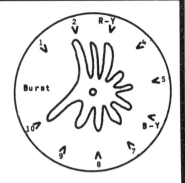

Fig. 11-21. Vectorscope pattern showing waveform "arms" in proper amplitude and phase for 90° modulation system.

Fig. 11-22. Vectorscope pattern showing waveform "arms" and phasing for a 105° modulation system.

or hue control, set the control to its center range and adjust the burst amplifier plate transformer or phase adjustment until it does. The normal range of the tint or hue control should allow the R-Y arm to move about 30° in either direction as the tint control is rotated from center to either extreme.

Color sync, or AFPC, can also be set using the vectorscope by slowly decreasing the color-bar generator output until the pattern starts to rotate. If the pattern rotates before the generator level drops below its 50% output point, the AFPC should be adjusted. Refer to the TV manufacturer's instructions. Normally the burst transformer or AFPC adjustment is set to slow the pattern down as much as possible. This puts the oscillator on the proper frequency.

CHAPTER 12

Maintenance

Since test instruments are also electronic equipment they can "go wrong," too! Because we depend on our test instruments to check faults in other equipment, it's especially important that they be kept in good condition and properly calibrated.

Most test instrument trouble falls into two categories: those that have an immediately noticeable effect, and the more subtle types that mislead your diagnosis because you may not know they are there. If a tube in your scope burns out you are likely to find out at once. An open multiplier resistor in a VTVM shows up just as quick. But if a tube begins to lose emission, or if the resistance of a multiplier increases 10%, you can go on innocently depending on the instrument, blaming the equipment you are testing rather than the test equipment itself.

So, it's easy to see why it pays to make sure our instruments are properly operating. Fortunately, most test equipment is relatively simple (even a DC scope is simpler that the TV set we use it with) to repair. But since much test equipment servicing will be testing the accuracy of the instrument—calibrating it—we must have some kind of standard to check it against. So our first job is to set up some standards.

CALIBRATION STANDARDS

The best standard is an accurate device of the type you are checking. If you can compare your voltmeter with a laboratory type, you are in luck. And once you have calibrated your voltmeter, you can use it to check other instruments, calibrate the vertical deflection of your scope, etc. But we don't all have access to instruments so good they can be used as standards. So we may have to do what the laboratories do when they calibrate their standard instruments. Use fundamental standards! We normally have only three quantities to measure in electronics servicing: volts, ohms, and amperes (or portions thereof). And if we have two known quantities, we can use them to get the third. (There are, of course, test instruments that measure frequency, but these are specialized units requiring specialized standards.)

Of the three, the standard ohm is the easiest to obtain. Wirewound 1% resistors are about $1 each. A little better job, marked "precision," can be bought for less than $1.50. And since most of your instruments are supposed to be accurate within 5%, a 1% calibrating resistor is accurate enough. More precision would be fine, but the price of a resistor jumps from $1 to about $8 when you increase the precision to 0.1%, and to around $30 if you want .01%.

Our practical ancestors had a statistical way to get precision. They averaged! To get a standard foot, they rounded up 16 men selected in sequence as they came out of church on Sunday morning. They had them stand in line heal to toe, measured the distance covered, and called it 16 feet. If you can measure a number of resistors (easy if you are a good friend of the dealer) and reject those that deviate from the average, you will find yourself with resistors a lot more accurate than 1%.

A 1,000-ohm resistor is a good standard for calibrating an ohmmeter. You need a couple more for convenience, say a 10-ohm and a 100,000-ohm. (A complete decade: 1, 10, 100, and so on to 1 megohm would be ideal.) But with a few resistors and a Wheatstone bridge (or another ohmmeter) you can build up your own resistor decades (ten resistors of each value). The ohmmeter doesn't have to be accurate—you are using it simply to compare resistors with your standard.

Now we have one quantity. How about a second? We have an excellent voltage standard in the Mallory mercury cell. Its voltage is usually constant at 1.357 volts (conservatively described in the catalogs as 1.35 volts). Another mercury cell has a percentage of manganese dioxide added to its mercuric oxide and is rated at 1.4 volts. The 1.35-volt type is a better standard over a period of time. It can be identified by the suffix "R" added to the type number (RM-12R, RM-42R, etc.).

Mercury cells are affected by shelf life, but not much. They drop off slowly to about 1.355 in about three months and to about 1.352 in a year, after which time the drop is much slower. (Note well that the drop from 1.36 to 1.35 is less than 1%.) So if you take the voltage of a new mercury cell as 1.355 and an older one as 1.350, you will be within precision limits—that is, if you have anything in the shop that will measure .05 volt DC. There are also test instruments called "voltage calibrators" available. These may use precision batteries or have a DC power supply with precision outputs.

With known voltage and resistance standards, we can measure the third unknown—current. For the moment, let us follow the instructions in the kit manuals and set our standards "aside for use later."

MULTIMETER MAINTENANCE

Maintenance of the common portable service instrument, the VOM or VTVM, is usually necessitated by two chief causes —rough handling and overload. Treat your equipment kindly! The bearings on your meter movement are much like those in a watch. Rough handling can crack or break them. Dropping the instrument not only puts a strain on the delicate bearings, but on other parts as well. The probes and leads also call for considerate handling and attention. A lead that breaks inside a probe at a moment when you are in a hurry may cause a diagnosis of "no voltage" and make you pull a chassis unnecessarily if you get in a hurry and forget to recheck the meter. But the multi-meter is pretty rugged and can stand a good deal of abuse, so the greater cause of its troubles comes from overload—overheated or burned-out resistors, damaged meter movements or springs, and the like.

If the meter appears to be defective while reading resistance, check it on AC and DC. Also, inspect the instrument for visable physical damage. If the trouble is obviously in the meter (pointer stuck half way down the scale, visibly burnt coils, etc.) replace it or send it to the manufacturer for repair. Meter repair is a field all it's own, and if you are a competent meter man you won't need to read this.

If the meter movement appears normal, check the multiplier. First look for burned resistors. Disconnect the multiplier at the meter end and (if you have access to another ohmmeter) measure the resistance of the various resistors in the string. If you don't have another ohmmeter handy, hook

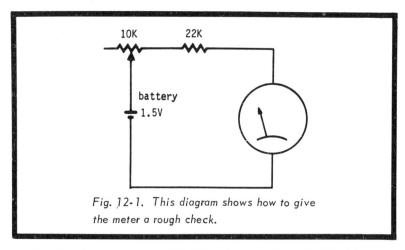

Fig. 12-1. This diagram shows how to give the meter a rough check.

a 30,000-ohm resistor (22,000-ohm unit and a 10,000-ohm pot) in series with a flashlight cell and test the meter as shown in Fig. 12-1. If the meter seems to act normally, the trouble is probably in the multipliers. Replace the multiplier resistors with carbon units of near the right value until the meter readings are approximately correct. Then you will have to calibrate.

But before going on to calibrate, let's note that the VTVM is a little different. It contains other electronic equipment and we have to make sure the tube is good and being supplied with proper voltages before going further. And since it is protected, the possibility of a burned-out meter is remote. Notice also that the VTVM's lowest scale is the one with the most resistance and that we have a series resistor in the probe.

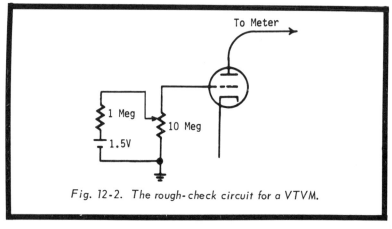

Fig. 12-2. The rough-check circuit for a VTVM.

So we hook up (for most VTVMs) a 10-megohm resistor in place of the meter multiplier and a 1-megohm resistor in series with the dry cell, as in Fig. 12-2. If meter action is normal, check and replace each of the multiplier resistors in turn until you find the defective one.

General Calibration

Begin with the lowest range, often 1.5 volts. If calibration is necessary, be sure to check the internal batteries and set the meter needle pointer to its rest position with the small adjustment screw on the meter face. If the multiplier bank was damaged by overload, some of the resistors may be good and others not. If we have an older instrument that has been over-

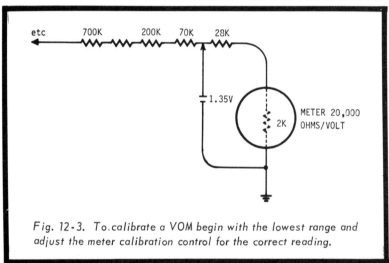

Fig. 12-3. To calibrate a VOM begin with the lowest range and adjust the meter calibration control for the correct reading.

loaded, we may not be sure whether the meter itself is accurate or not.

In the case of multiplier damage, use the substitute multiplier string, indicated earlier, along with the operator's manual you got with the instrument. Or, you may calculate the value of the resistors with the help of the information in Chapter 3. Remember, the resistance of your meter must be allowed for, at least on the lower ranges. Now get out your mercury cell or other "voltage calibrating standard and try it across the first resistor as in Fig. 12-3. The meter should read very close to the value of the standard. If it doesn't, adjust the calibration control found on all but the simplest VOMs until you get an exact reading. If your meter is very old, it may have lost some of its magnetism over the years, but may still be quite linear and usable. We'll deal with that case when we talk about old meters. Now your meter should be good on all ranges if you have picked your multiplier resistors carefully and accurately.

Partial multiplier burnout is often caused by putting a high voltage on one of the low ranges of a VOM—say 250 volts on the 10-volt range. (It is almost impossible to burn out a VTVM, with its 11-megohm or higher input resistance.) So all you have to do is proceed as if you had a completely burned-out string to replace the damaged resistors of the 10-volt and lower ranges. The resistors for the higher ranges have not been damaged, so they can be re-connected and your meter is good again.

Calibrating a meter that is suspected of being inaccurate is a little harder. Again, you start as in Fig. 12-1, but using a standard voltage and your own secondary standard resistors to check a low scale. Your reading is likely to be either correct or low. If correct, any inaccuracy is in the multiplier resistors. If low, the meter magnet may be weak, you may have trouble in the bearings, or the coil or springs may have been damaged by overload. In the last two cases, about the only thing you can do is replace the meter or have it repaired.

If the meter reads low, but seems reasonably linear, try the standard cell on the 1.5- and 5-volt scales. If it reads the same voltage regardless of whether it is on the high or low scale, it may be worthwhile to make a new multiplier. First (assuming you have no other meter for comparison) find the correct resistance for the lowest range. For example, suppose the 1.5-volt range reads 10% low. The 30,000-ohm resistor in that range will have to be decreased to about 27,000 ohms. (The actual resistance of the meter itself will enter into the problem, of course.) A little figuring (or a parallel-resistance chart) shows that a 300,000-ohm resistor across the 30,000-ohm one will give us an almost exact figure.

There are two (or more) ways to check higher voltage scales. Having checked out (or calibrated) our lowest range resistor as in Fig. 12-3, we can now check the higher scales. Connect four flashlight cells (in series) or a 6-volt standard to the meter to check the 10-volt range. If we have an adjustable DC

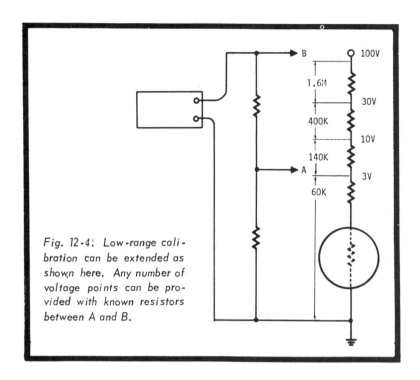

*Fig. 12-4. Low-range cali-
bration can be extended as
shown here. Any number of
voltage points can be provided with known resistors
between A and B.*

power supply, we can use the approach shown in Fig. 12-4.
A string of 1000-ohm resistors—calibrated by your standards
—can be hooked up and the voltage across the first one checked
on the 10-volt scale. If the voltage is adjusted to give 10 volts
at that point, you have taps at 10-volt intervals to 100. (Incidentally, an AC-DC radio power supply furnishes about 120
volts DC, which can be dropped below 100 volts by using a
variable transformer (Variac, etc.) in the AC line).

The setup in Fig. 12-4 was made with four power resistors:
250, 750, 4000 and 5000 ohms. The voltage taps at 250 ohms
(A) was checked on the 3-volt scale of the meter. When the
supply is adjusted to give exactly 2.5 volts at that tap, the top
of the resistor string (B) will be exactly 100 volts (and you
also have a reading at 50 volts). Once the 100-volt range is
calibrated, the 250-volt range can be checked at 100 volts.

Another way to check the meter on higher ranges is to shunt
it with a resistance equal to its own. This may vary anywhere
from 600 to 5000 ohms (including the meter calibrating resistor). Use a variable resistor covering this resistance
range, and with the meter on the calibrated 100-volt scale,

adjust the variable resistor until your measured 100 volts reads 50. Now all readings on the meter will be doubled to give the true voltage. Check a voltage that reads as high on the scale as you can, say 180 (90 volts on your modified meter). Take off the shunt, switch to the 250-volt range and see if it reads 180 volts.

Calibrating The VTVM

Fortunately, most VTVMs are stable, relatively rugged, and easy to calibrate. They have calibrating controls (internal) for AC-zero, AC volts, positive and negative DC, and often a low-voltage DC adjustment.

The VTVM uses a 1.5-volt battery to measure resistance and it should be replaced if the meter will not adjust to full scale with the ohmmeter leads shorted together. The procedure for calibrating a VTVM somewhat follows that suggested for a VOM, except there are more adjustments. A VTVM can be calibrated on negative DC by setting the range selector to a low range (5v) and connecting the meter to a standard voltage source (between 3 and 5 volts). Since you are calibrating the negative DC section, connect the ground lead to the positive terminal of the voltage source. Adjust the negative DC adjustment to set the meter at the proper value.

Calibration of the positive DC scale is the same except the meter ground lead goes to the standard voltage ground terminal. Calibrating the AC scales of a VTVM normally involves two adjustments—AC zero and an AC calibrating control. The meter is first zero'd with the AC-zero control. In VTVMs using dual rectifier tubes, a defective or weak tube can prevent balance. Try swapping them around: if that doesn't work, replace them.

Common Errors

The common mistake of trying to check the resistance of a circuit without realizing the power is turned on frequently makes the ohmmeter the victim of overload. (When we know there is a voltage in the circuit, we usually look at the meter to see if it's on a reasonable range.) The result is the same as with an overloaded voltmeter—damage to the meter, or multiplier resistors burned out or damaged by heat. The remedy is to use caution and turn the power off before measuring resistance.

Also, watch those probe leads. Many technicians point out that the resistance in the leads is unimportant; it is cancelled out by the zero adjustment. But they overlook the fact that the zero adjustment is falsified—it is supposed to be made with zero ohms; therefore, it is not exact. (If the VTVM is zero'd with too much resistance in the leads, it may not even go to full scale on open circuit.)

SCOPE SERVICING

The oscilloscope is a delicate and complex instrument in itself and operates much like a television set as far as sweep and high-voltage circuits are concerned. Its main problems are caused by tube aging, though it can present any of the probable defects of amplifiers.

Since a scope is like a TV set in some respects, you can apply some of the same troubleshooting procedures. For example: a loss of high voltage will result in no visible beam on the CRT; loss of vertical or horizontal sweep will be as obvious as it is in a TV set; loss of a vertical or horizontal amplifier will also be evident, as there will be no gain on these respective functions; poor rectifiers will cause a loss of focus and brightness, and leaky filters will cause hum. A little understanding of your particular scope can go a long way toward diagnosing its own illnesses.

Once you have checked the scope's principle actions you can check to see if the tubes are in good condition. This is particularly true of the rectifier tube, since troubles with the CR tube may really be due to low voltage. When new tubes are put in a scope, the circuits in which they are placed usually have to be readjusted. This is particularly true of critical circuits (oscillators and sweep). Keep the tubes turned on (age them) at least 24 hours before making any adjustments.

Two troubles that may be due to low-emission tubes are vertical and horizontal nonlinearity. Vertical linearity can be checked with the hookup in Fig. 12-5. Connect a source of AC (your audio generator, the audio section of the bench generator, or even the calibration control of the scope itself) to the horizontal and vertical inputs of the scope. Turn up the controls till you get a diagonal line not more than about two inches long (inside the square on the graticule if you have a graticule ruled to show the limits of vertical amplification).

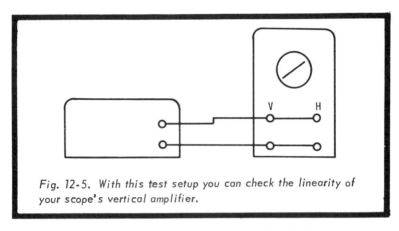

Fig. 12-5. With this test setup you can check the linearity of your scope's vertical amplifier.

The line should be absolutely straight. Vertical nonlinearity —failure to amplify at higher levels—is manifested by the familiar sharp bend at the ends of the line, identical with the trace that shows the same weakness in an amplifier.

Horizontal nonlinearity can be revealed by turning the frequency control from EXT (where you had it for the vertical linearity test) to a low frequency that will give you four to six waves on the screen. Nonlinearity is indicated in Fig. 12-6 —the waves are crowded as the sweep voltage fails to rise to its proper maximum.

Nonlinearity may be caused by the input circuits—the frequency-compensating capacitors may be misadjusted or defective. In that case the straight line in Fig. 12-5 will have a definite hook on one end. Adjust the capacitor until the line straightens out. If it won't, try replacing the capacitor.

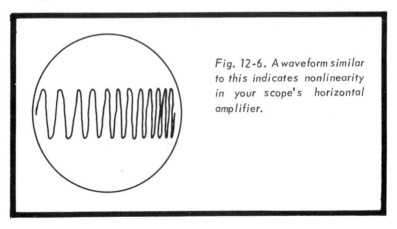

Fig. 12-6. A waveform similar to this indicates nonlinearity in your scope's horizontal amplifier.

The high-voltage power supply puts a strain on resistors and capacitors. Changes in resistance and capacitance may make difficulties in centering, or even take the spot off the screen altogether.

Other internal adjustments also require attention as the tubes age. The astigmatism adjustment keeps the spot focused as it approaches the edge of the screen. It interacts with the intensity and focus controls as shown in Fig. 12-7, the astigmatism, focus and intensity circuitry of an Eico 435/DC scope. Always adjust the astigmatism control with moderate intensity circuitry and with the focus control set for sharp focus at the center of the screen. Go over the adjustment of

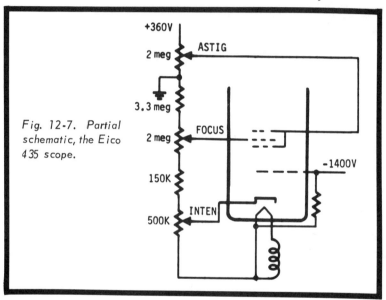

Fig. 12-7. Partial schematic, the Eico 435 scope.

these three controls several times. Higher-priced scopes have a number of other adjustments which are covered in detail in the service manual for each instrument.

A scope can be used to accurately indicate voltages if properly calibrated. Many scopes provide an internal calibrating voltage for this very purpose, or you can use a standard similar to that shown in Fig. 12-8. The vertical input is calibrated in peak-to-peak values which are read on a graduated screen or "grid" supplied with the scope. The scope's vertical amplifier has an attenuator switch for this which sets the level on the scope to indicate at 1 volt, 10 volts, etc., on the grid.

Fig. 12-8. The problem of voltage calibration can be simplified with one of these reference standards.

For example: if a one-volt source (internal or external) is fed to the scope's vertical amplifier, you can adjust the attenuator controls to make that 1 volt read at full scale on the graduated grid. Then leave the controls alone and measure the voltages you want to check. If it is more than 1 volt in amplitude, switch the vertical attenuator to the X10 position and now full scale is 10 volts. If the trace shows only half-scale deflection you know you have a 5-volt signal. This is an essential capability when accurate signal levels must be measured, as in TV horizontal oscillator and output stages.

One other problem should not be overlooked—external magnetic fields. My scope suddenly went wrong late one evening, the trace sinking slowly out of sight at the bottom of the tube face as soon as the scope warmed up. I started troubleshooting the next day after first clearing off the work bench. The scope was absolutely OK! I realized that the last thing I had close to the scope was a large loudspeaker with an equally large magnetic field. Apparently I had pushed the scope toward it the night before to make room without noticing it.

SIGNAL GENERATORS

The bench signal generator is usually a simple device that

is easily kept operating, though not always easily kept on frequency. It requires maintenance just like other instruments due to aging of components. Most of these generators can be easily calibrated because every broadcast station is a reference with a frequency stability of far greater accuracy than you will be able to use in calibrating. To calibrate the bench generator for frequencies below the broadcast band, set the broadcast receiver to 910 kHz. There are nearly 50 stations on that frequency scattered over the country and waiting to act as yardsticks. Tune the generator to half that frequency, 455 kHz. If it is accurate, you will hear the second harmonic right on 910. If it is OK on 455, set the generator at 300 kHz (303, if you can read it!) and you should hear the third harmonic on 910. You should also hear a signal on 910 kHz with the generator tuned to 225 kHz (again, 227.5 if you want to be exact) on your generator. You may have to couple the generator output close to the receiver antenna.

If the signal generator frequency is not correct, it will have to be calibrated. Most generators have trimmers and/or coils for each frequency range. If there is only a trimmer capacitor, it is usually adjusted at a point somewhere in the upper portion of the frequency range of the band. Read the manufacturer's instructions. To calibrate the broadcast coil, for example, tune in a station near 1200 and adjust the capacitor. If there is a capacitor and a tuned coil, adjust the capacitor near 1600 kHz and the coil slug near 600 kHz. Then go over the 1600-kHz adjustment again. If there is only a tuned coil, calibrate the generator somewhere near the middle of the various ranges. (Except for the band that includes the common 455-kHz intermediate frequency. That is the important point on the band, so adjust the circuit at 455 kHz. If the rest of the scale can be made absolutely correct, so much the better.)

On the shortwave bands you may have to take the frequencies you can get, even if they don't fall on the best parts of the scale. WWV, at Boulder, Colorado, transmits on 2.5, 5, and multiples of 5 MHz. (Occasionally you will hear WWVH in Hawaii on the same frequencies.) CHU, Ottawa, Canada, transmits on 3.33, 7.335, and 14.670 MHz. Shortwave broadcast stations announce their transmitting frequencies regularly. Even without a shortwave receiver, you can calibrate the signal generator with a television receiver. The funda-

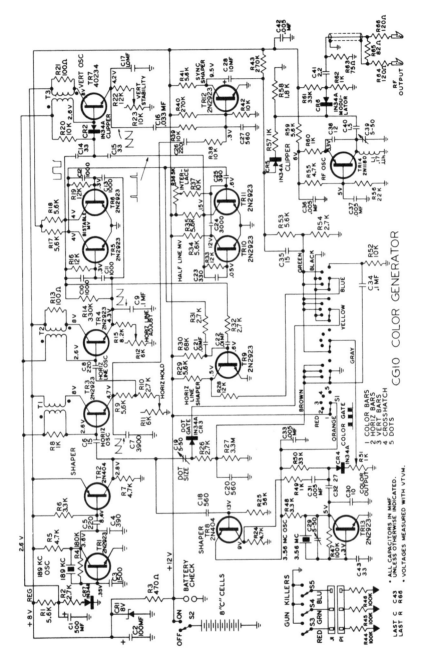

Fig. 12-9. Schematic diagram of Sencore's CG10 transistorized color-bar generator. (Courtesy Sencore, Inc.)

mental is unmistakeable on the TV screen, and a second harmonic can usually be detected.

OTHER EQUIPMENT

Tube checkers, power packs, and similar equipment have only the troubles common to all electronic equipment. Resistors or capacitors may change value, tubes wear out, and wire connections break with rough use or manipulation during use. The modern test instruments we have today are for the most part quite reliable with normal routine maintenance. But to modify an old farmer's proverb: Keep your equipment up and it will keep you up!

COLOR-BAR GENERATOR CALIBRATION METHODS

Most color-bar generators today provide a standard 10-bar pattern output using a crystal-controlled master oscillator as a pulse generator source. The circuit diagram of Fig. 12-9 shows a Sencore transistorized generator. A color-bar generator is actually a small TV station that can transmit signals in the low VHF bands. This particular generator operates from a 189-kHz master oscillator (TR1) which is used to provide the basic pulses. It is helpful to understand how a unit like this operates in order to properly adjust and maintain it. So we will briefly describe its operation, then adjust and calibrate it. Signals from the oscillator are shaped into the correct waveform by TR2 and TR8 before being fed to the first counter stage, TR3. This stage divides the 189-kHz signal by 12 to produce the horizontal line frequency. The output of TR3 is used to develop horizontal sync pulses in TR12 and also to trigger the next counter stage, TR4. TR4 then divides the 15,750-Hz signal from TR3 alternately by 17 and 18 which is controlled by a multivibrator (MV) stage, TR5 and TR6, through R14. The 450-Hz MV output goes to TR7 through C14. At the same time, a second source of pulses, also at 450 Hz, are fed to TR7 through C15 from the half-line MV, TR10 and TR11. However, pulses from the second source arrive approximately half way during the first source of pulses and the result is that when they are "mixed" in TR7, they appear as a single source of 900-Hz pulses. The third counting stage (TR7) then divides by 15 to produce a vertical frequency of 60 Hz. TR7 is used to develop sync pulses in TR12.

The half-line MV triggers each time TR4 divides by 17 and generates a new pulse 20 to 40 microseconds later which is controlled by INTERLACE control R36. Since TR7 locks to this source of pulses through C15, every other time it fires (it divides by an odd number) one field (as viewed on a TV raster) can be shifted with respect to the other field approximately plus or minus 10 microseconds.

The outputs from the collectors of TR5 and TR6 are then mixed together to form the horizontal line pulses in TR9. Since the bistable MV switches each time TR4 fires, the horizontal lines pulses are also generated at the same rate; i.e., spaced alternately by 17 and 18 horizontal lines. Thus, they always begin at the start of the horizontal sync pulse. The width of the horizontal line pulse is determined by R30, C21, and C22.

Signals from color-signal oscillator TR13, which is triggered at a 189-kHz rate through CR4, appear across the COLOR OUTPUT control R51 when the function switch S1 is in the color-bar pattern. When S1 is in any other position, supply voltage is removed from the color oscillator and shaper TR8 to prevent spurious operation. Color signals from R51, vertical line or dot signals from CR3, and horizontal line signals from TR9 are selected with function switch S1 individually or in combination (depending on the pattern selected) and are mixed with the composite sync signal from TR12 across CR5, R57, and R58. C35 and R53 help to isolate the signal sources from the composite sync signal. CR5 clips the negative-going sync signal to that the sync amplitude across R57 and R58 is approximately the same as the positive signal amplitude at this point. The total peak-to-peak amplitude of the composite signal across R58 is approximately .3 volts.

RF oscillator RT14 is tunable from 55 to 84 MHz (Channels 2 through 6) with C39. The output from the collector is amplitude-modulated by the composite video signal in modulator diode CR6. Modulated RF is coupled through C41 to the RF output cable, which is terminated with a resistive pad to match the 300-ohm input of a TV receiver.

The power supply for the CG10 consists of eight "C" size batteries. All stages operate directly from the 12-volt supply except 189-kHz master oscillator TR1, shaper stage TR2, and the three counters, TR3, TR4, and TR7. Supply voltage to these stages is regulated at 8 volts with zener diode CR1.

CR10 TROUBLE CHART

Symptom	Probable Cause	Corrective Measure
No color bars	3.56-MHz crystal, TR13, or CR4	Check transistor and diode. Replace crystal.
Color but no bars	TR8, C18, C31	Check transistor and C18 and C31.
RF OK but weak or no modulation.	CR5, TR12, C28	Check transistor and diode. Check C28 for open or short.
No RF	TR14, CR6, C39	Check transistor and diode. Check C39 for short.
No vertical bars or dots	CR3	Check diode for open.
No vertical sync	CR2, TR7, T3, TR12	Check transistors and diode. Check T3 with ohmmeter.
No vertical or horizontal sync	TR12, C28	Check transistor. Check C28 for open.
No horizontal lines	TR9	Check transistor.
Horizontal lines cut off before end of raster	C21, C22	Check for open.
Interlace control has no effect.	TR10, TR11, C24	Check transistors. Check C24 for open.
Unit will not operate after replacing batteries	Battery holder contacts	Check battery holder contacts for corrosion. Check to be sure they are making contact.
Unit completely unstable	CR1, CR7, Batteries, C1 C2	Check CR1 and CR7. Check battery voltage (see "Checking batteries"). Check C1 and C2 for leakage or short.

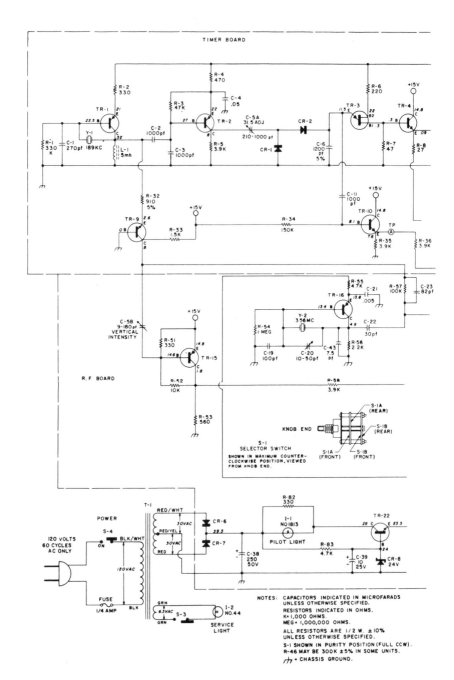

Fig. 12-10. Schematic diagram of the Knight KG-685 solid-state

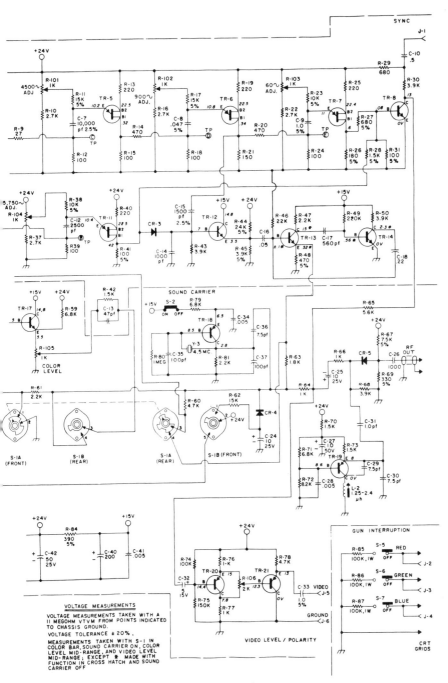

color-bar generator. (Courtesy Allied Radio)

Dot Size

The color-bar generator circuit in Fig. 12-9 has several adjustments. One of these is the DOT SIZE which is accessible from the bottom of the unit. DOT SIZE adjustment C19 changes the dot width, the vertical lines in the dot, crosshatch, and vertical line patterns. The smaller the dots, the easier it is to see errors in the color TV convergence. However, the dots should not be made so small that they can't be clearly seen. They should be adjusted to the desired size while watching the pattern on a TV set. After making the adjustment, check the vertical lines to be sure they are not too small to be usable.

Color Frequency

The color subcarrier must be accurate, and it can be adjusted by using the burst signal from a color program. Tune in a color program on a normally operating set. Remove the correction voltage to the 3.58-MHz oscillator in the TV set (refer to the TV set manufacturer's schematic). Adjust the reference oscillator in the TV until a beat is seen in the picture or the colors are holding sync. Then connect the color generator to the TV set VHF antenna terminals and set it for the correct channel. Adjust the generator for a color-bar pattern. With the TV set correction voltage still disconnected, tune color phase adjustment C29 for a zero beat in the color-bar pattern. It is wise to repeat this procedure a couple of times.

RF Oscillator

The RF oscillator in this unit is pretuned to 67.25 MHz (Channel 4). If a TV channel in your area operates on the RF oscillator frequency, it is best to set the generator to an unused channel. On this unit channels 2, 3, 5, and 6 are available, but a frequency standard should be used when tuning it to another channel to insure accuracy. A color TV also can be used by switching it to one of the unused channels without touching the fine tuning. Then connect the color generator to the VHF antenna terminals and set it to provide color bars.

Adjust the RF frequency on the generator until a color-bar pattern appears properly displayed. Then check the other patterns to be sure they are also properly tuned.

GENERATOR ALIGNMENT WITH SCOPE AND TV

Another color-bar generator, the Knight KG-685, is shown in the schematic diagram of Fig. 12-10. This unit is also transistorized and uses counter-divider stages to produce the necessary pattern pulses. Adjustment and calibration adjustments are made using an oscilloscope to check the various frequency waveforms at several stages throughout the circuit.

In this unit the scope is connected to test point A (emitter of TR10) and set to display two cycles of the 15,750-Hz frequency. The scope is calibrated to the voltages indicated in the waveforms in Figs. 12-11 to 12-13. Then trimmer A (31.5 kHz) is adjusted to produce the six-step waveform in Fig. 12-11A. Move the scope to test point B and adjust control B (15,750 kHz) for two pulses per cycle as shown in Fig. 12-11B. Adjust the scope's sweep frequency to display five complete cycles as shown. All five should be the same.

Now move the scope lead to test point C and adjust the sweep frequency. Adjust control E (60-Hz) for a waveform containing 15 pulses as shown in Fig. 12-11E. As noted before, the 15 pulses may not be visible, but when correctly adjusted the pattern will be stationary or drift very slowly across the screen. If the scope patterns move fast with a definite 15 count, then one of the preceeding counter stages is misadjusted. Not all color-bar generators provide for frequency adjustment of the counter stages, but this explanation will give you an idea of how they are aligned and what to look for.

RF Adjustment

The RF output of this generator can be set for Channels 3, 4, or 5; pick an unused channel for operation in your particular area. Place the pattern selector to the color-bar position. If the 3.56-MHz oscillator in the generator needs adjustment, turn trimmer C20 on the RF circuit board in tight. Then back it out one turn; this is just a rough setting. Adjust the CHANNEL coil for a color pattern on the channel you selected, turning the coil counter-clockwise until the pattern

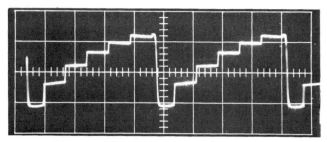

TEST POINT — A
5V per CM

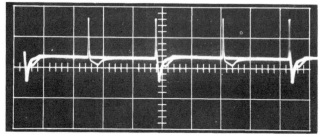

TEST POINT — B
1V per CM

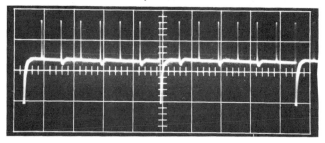

TEST POINT — C
1V per CM

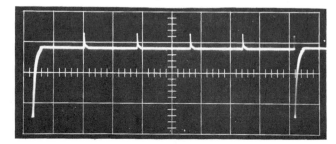

TEST POINT — D
2V per CM

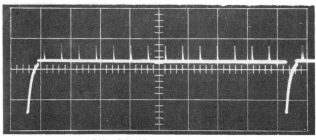

TEST POINT — E 2V per CM

Fig. 12-11. Oscilloscope waveforms at various points in the
KG-685 timer circuits. (Also see opposite page)

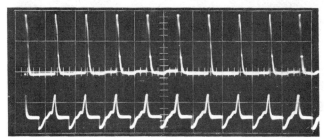

BASE OF TR-12 (LO-CAP PROBE)

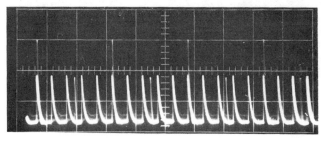

UPPER (COLLECTOR TR-15) LOWER (BASE OF TR-15) (LO-CAP PROBE)

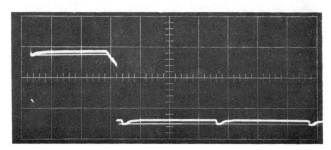

EMITTER TR-13

Fig. 12- 12. Oscilloscope waveform at TR15 (A); oscilloscope
waveform at TR12 (B); waveform at TR13.

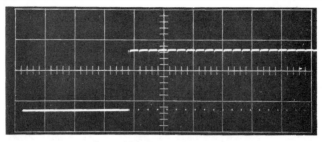

SYNC (COMP. VIDEO JACK)

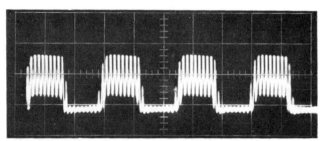

SLIDER R-105 COLOR LEVEL

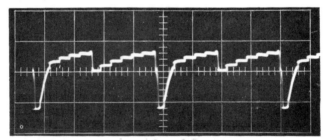

GRAYSCALE TRACKING (COMP. VIDEO JACK)

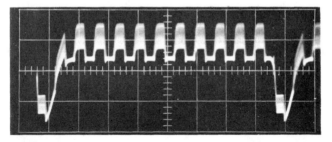

COLOR BARS (COMP. VIDEO JACK)

Fig. 12-13. Oscilloscope waveforms taken at various signal jacks.

appears on the TV screen. NOTE: There are two points on the channel coil where the pattern can appear because modulation is present on the low and high sidebands of the picture carrier. Adjusting the CHANNEL coil for the "low side" of the channel will automatically put the color subcarrier at the right spot on the TV receiver's bandpass curve.

Adjusting the 3.56-MHz Oscillator

An approximate adjustment of the oscillator as previously mentioned can be made by turning C20 in tight, then backing it out one turn. To set this oscillator correctly, use a normally-operating color TV receiver. The TV receiver's 3.58-MHz reference oscillator should also be calibrated to insure proper adjustment of the generator and the method for this is explained in the next section. Set the generator's COLOR LEVEL control to normal. Then short the TV receiver's 3.58-MHz reactance oscillator grid test point to ground. (Check the TV manufacturer's schematic for this point.) Adjust trimmer capacitor C20 in the RF circuit so the color is standing still or moves very slowly across the screen. This should put the generator to within a few cycles of the exact 3.56-MHz frequency. Remove the short from the grid of the TV set's 3.58-MHz oscillator; the pattern should be locked in.

3.58-MHz Oscillator Calibration (Color TV Receiver)

Turn the TV receiver to a station transmitting color. Adjust the HUE and SATURATION controls for a normal picture and natural flesh tones. Short the grid of the TV set's reference oscillator to ground (consult the manufacturer's test data). Adjust the reactance coil for a zero beat in the picture. When you are within a cycle or two of 3.58-MHz, the picture will stand still or drift slowly across the screen. Color does not occur in bars at zero beat, but will seem stationary at 60-Hz intervals away from the correct frequency. Now remove the short from the grid. The color should lock in. Check the range of the receiver's tint control; the color should stay locked in at all settings.

Appendix

This table of preferred values is helpful in selecting and combining resistors for instrument use. Values down to 5% are available in practically all electronic stores and mail-order supply houses. The 1% type is not as available, though the mail-order houses list them in their industrial catalogs. At least one company (Newark) offers resistors on special order, at precision tolerances greater than 1%. Thus, for a line of 1% resistors that sell between 90¢ and $1.50 each, resistors rated at 0.5% may be obtained by adding 100% to listed prices and for 0.1% add an additional 200%, etc.

Large, wire-wound power resistors are more commonly listed according to the ancient specifications than in preferred values For example, you may obtain them at 10, 15, and 25 ohms and often at 18, 22, and 27 ohms. To arrive at in-between values, like 20 and 25 ohms, sometimes it's easier to series and parallel several resistors, though exact values are seldom needed in power resistors, except for calibration.

Notice that with 1% resistors, as in others, it is often possible to pick several closer to the rated 1% values if you have equipment that will measure them.

TABLE OF PREFERRED VALUES

5%	10%	20%	1% Values			
100	100	100	100	102	105	107
110			110	113	115	118
120	120		121	124	127	130
130			133	137	140	143
150	150	150	147	150	154	158
160			162	165	169	174
180	180		178	182	187	191
200			196	200	205	210
220	220	220	215	221	226	232
240			237	243	249	255
270	270		261	267	274	280
300			287	294	301	309
330	330	330	316	324	332	340
360			348	357	265	374
390	390		383	392	402	412
430			422	432	442	453
470	470	470	464	475	487	499
510			511	523	546	549
560	560		562	576	590	604
620			619	634	649	665
680	680	680	681	698	715	732
750			750	768	787	806
820	820		825	845	866	887
910			909	931	953	976
1K	1K	1K	1K			

DECIBEL TABLE

db, voltage, current ratios	Gain (+)	Gain (-)	% Attenuation	db, power ratios
1	1.12	0.89	11	
2	1.26	0.79	21	1
3	1.41	0.70	30	
4	1.58	0.63	37	2
6	2.0	0.50	50	3
8	2.5	0.40	60	4
10	3.16	0.31	69	5
12	4.0	0.25	75	6
14	5.0	0.20	80	7
16	6.3	0.16	84	8
18	8.0	0.13	88	9
20	10	0.1	90	10
22	12.5	.08	92	11
24	16	.0625	94	12
26	20	.05	95	13

14	96	.04	25	28
15	96.7	.0325	32	30
16	97.5	.025	40	32
17	98	.02	50	34
18	98.4	.016	63	36
19	98.75	.0125	80	38
20	99	.01	100	40
21	99.2	.008	125	42
22	99.4	.006	158	44
23	99.5	.005	200	46
24	99.6	.004	250	48
25	99.7	.003	300	50
26	99.75	.0025	400	52
27	99.8	.002	500	54
28	99.84	.0016	631	56
29	99.87	.00125	794	58
30	99.9	.001	1000	60

DECIBEL TABLE, SMALL SIGNAL RATIOS

Db, voltage or current ratios	Gain (+)	Gain (-)	Attenuation (%)	db, power ratios
0.1	1.012	.988	1.2	0
0.2	1.023	.977	2.3	0.1
0.3	1.035	.966	3.4	
0.4	1.047	.955	4.5	0.2
0.5	1.059	.944	5.6	
0.6	1.072	.933	6.7	0.3
0.7	1.084	.922	7.8	
0.8	1.097	.911	8.9	0.4
0.9	1.109	.901	9.9	
1.0	1.122	.891	11	0.5
1.2	1.148	.870	13	0.6
1.4	1.175	.851	15	0.7

DECIBEL TABLE, SMALL SIGNAL RATIOS

Db, voltage or current ratios	Gain (+)	Gain (-)	Attenuation (%)	db, power ratios
1.6	1.202	.831	17	0.8
1.8	1.230	.812	19	0.9
2.0	1.259	.794	20.6	1.0
2.2	1.288	.776	22	1.1
2.4	1.318	.759	24	1.2
2.6	1.349	.741	26	1.3
2.8	1.380	.724	28	1.4
3.0	1.413	.708	29	1.5

TV CHANNEL INFORMATION

Ch. No.	Channel Limits	Picture Carrier	Sound Carrier
All Frequencies in Megahertz			
2	54-60	55.25	59.75
3	60-66	61.25	65.75
4	66-72	67.25	71.75
5	76-82	77.25	81.25
6	82-88	83.25	87.75
7	174-180	175.25	179.75
8	180-196	181.25	185.75
9	186-192	187.25	191.75
10	192-198	193.25	197.75
11	198-204	199.25	203.75
12	204-210	205.25	209.75
13	210-216	211.25	215.75
14	470-476	471.25	475.75
15	476-482	477.25	481.75
16	482-488	483.25	487.75
17	488-494	489.25	493.75
18	494-500	495.25	499.75
19	500-506	501.25	505.75
20	506-512	507.25	511.75
21	512-518	513.25	517.75
22	518-524	519.25	523.75
23	524-530	525.25	529.75
24	530-536	531.25	535.75
25	536-542	537.25	541.75
26	542-548	543.25	547.75
27	548-554	549.25	553.75
28	554-560	555.25	559.75
29	560-566	561.25	565.75
30	566-572	567.25	571.75
31	572-578	573.25	577.75

Ch. No.	Channel Limits	Picture Carrier	Sound Carrier
32	578-584	579.25	583.75
33	584-590	585.25	589.75
34	590-596	591.25	595.75
35	596-602	597.25	601.75
36	602-608	603.25	607.75
37	608-614	609.25	613.75
38	614-620	615.25	619.75
39	620-626	621.25	625.75
40	626-632	627.25	631.75
41	632-638	633.25	637.75
42	638-644	639.25	643.75
43	644-650	645.25	649.75
44	650-656	651.25	655.75
45	656-662	657.25	661.75
46	662-668	663.25	667.75
47	668-674	669.25	673.75
48	674-680	675.25	679.75
49	680-686	681.25	685.75
50	686-692	687.25	691.75
51	692-698	693.25	697.75
52	698-704	699.25	703.75
53	704-710	705.25	709.75
54	710-716	711.25	715.75
55	716-722	717.25	721.75
56	722-728	723.25	727.75
57	728-734	729.25	733.75
58	734-740	735.25	739.75
59	740-746	741.25	745.75
60	746-752	747.25	751.75
61	752-758	753.25	757.75
62	758-764	759.25	763.75
63	764-770	765.25	769.75
64	770-776	771.25	775.75

Ch. No.	Channel Limits	Picture Carrier	Sound Carrier
65	776–782	777.25	781.75
66	782–788	783.25	787.75
67	788–794	789.25	793.75
68	794–800	795.25	799.75
69	800–806	801.25	805.75
70	806–812	807.25	811.75
71	812–818	813.25	817.75
72	818–824	819.25	823.75
73	824–830	825.25	829.75
74	830–836	831.25	835.75
75	836–842	837.25	841.75
76	842–848	843.25	847.75
77	848–854	849.25	853.75
78	854–860	855.25	859.75
79	860–866	861.25	865.75
80	866–872	867.25	871.75
81	872–878	873.25	877.75
82	878–884	879.25	873.75
83	884–890	885.25	889.75

CONVERSION — OUTPUT VOLTS TO WATTS

Watt	Voltage across voice coil		
	4 ohms	8 ohms	16 ohms
1	2	2.8	4
1.5	2.5	3.5	4.9
2	2.8	4	5.7
3	3.5	4.9	7
4	4	5.7	8
6	4.9	7	9.8
8	5.7	8	11.3
10	6.3	9	12.6
15	7.5	11	15.5
20	9	12.6	18
30	11	15.5	22
40	12.6	18	25
60	15.5	22	31

Glossary

AC - DC—Equipment that works on either direct or alternating current, usually small transformerless radios, but the term may also be used for small motors (more commonly called "universal).

AF - AFT—Audio frequency; audio frequency transformer.

AGC—Automatic gain control

Alignment—The process of tuning all the adjustable circuits in a piece of equipment to correct operating specifications.

Amplitude—The strength, level, power, or volume of a signal (Latin: amplitudo, size).

Attenuator—(Attenuate: to make weak). A device, usually a resistor or network of resistors, intended to reduce the strength of a signal. An attenuator on a signal generator may be calibrated accurately in decibels of attenuation.

Audio—Having to do with electric waves at frequencies within the human hearing range, or equipment which handles such waves.

AVC—Automatic volume control. Usually applied to circuitry that limits the RF gain in a radio receiver, thereby limiting the output.

B

Balance—Equality between two things; the act of making two things equal. Thus, you balance the channels of a stereo amplifier to get the same amount of sound out of each, or balance two output tubes so that each carries the same current.

Band—A range of frequencies normally devoted to some particular use. The broadcast band extends from 540 to 1600 kHz; the FM band from 88 to 108 MHz.

Band switch—The switch in a multi-range receiver or test instrument that changes its operation from one range of frequences to another.

Bandwidth — The range of frequencies covered by a device or component, such as the bandwidth of a bandpass filter.

Bar—A band on a TV screen wider than a line. It may be light, dark, or colored, of any width (though the tendency is to speak of broader bars as bands) and vertical or horizontal (occasionally we hear of diagonal bars due to faulty horizontal hold).

Bond—To connect together through a path having negligible resistance, as to bond the cable shields to the chassis.

Bridge—A network in which a meter or indicator is connected across two points that are at the same voltage when all the elements in the circuit are equal, or have a specific relation to each other.

Bridge—To shunt, as "bridge the suspected filter capacitor with a known good one."

B-Y (R-Y, G-Y)—In color TV the signal(s) that carries the color information (red, blue, and green). When mixed with the brightness (Y) signal (usually in the picture tube) it becomes the blue (or red, or green) signal.

C

Calibrate—To determine the correctness of the markings on a scale; to mark a scale with absolute values, as to calibrate a variable capacitor in pfd.

Capacimeter—An instrument for measuring capacitance. Applies to most capacitor checkers, though some of the simpler types indicate only quality and give no indication of capacitance.

Carrier—An RF wave that is modulated by a signal of a different frequency. The radio waves of the broadcast band, with frequencies from 540 to 1600 kHz, are carriers of audio signals ranging from about 30 to 15,000 Hz. The 7,000-Hz carrier of the intermodulation analyzer is modulated by a 60-Hz signal.

Conductance, mutual—The ratio of a small change in the plate current of a tube to the small change in grid voltage that produces it. (Usually called transconductance, except when tube testers are discussed.)

Convergence—Making the red, green, and blue images on the screen coincide exactly at all points on the screen. To the installer; divided into static convergence—making the beams from the three guns converge at the center of the screen—and dynamic convergence, adjusting the circuits that maintain convergence as the beam sweeps across the screen.

Converter—A circuit stage or element (tube, transistor, or diode) that changes signals of one frequency to signals of another frequency, usually by mixing them with waves of another frequency. (See mixer.)

Couple, coupling—To connect two circuits together; the equipment used to couple them. Circuits may be conductively coupled—with a piece of wire; inductively coupled—with a transformer; or capacitively coupled through a capacitor.

Core—The material inside an electrical winding. A 60-Hz transformer is wound on a silicon steel core; RF coils may have air or ferrite cores to increase their inductance, or even cores of brass or other non-ferrous metals, to reduce inductance.

CR, CR tube—Cathode ray, cathode-ray tube.

Cross-hatch—A pattern on a TV screen that consists of a

number of thin vertical and horizontal lines produced by a cross-hatch generator. When the lines are attenuated until they drop just below the visible level, the intersections are still seen and our cross-hatch generator has become a dot generator.

D

Decibel, db—(A tenth of a bel.) A unit of measurement that varies arithmetically as the value measured varies exponentially or geometrically. For example, a quantity with a value of 10 (say 10 watts) could be expressed as 10^1, or in common decibles as 1 bel (10 db) in comparison to 1 watt, which would then be 0 db. If increased to 100 watts we would have 10^2 or 2 bels (20 db) to 1000, 10^3 or 30 db, etc.

Deflection—The drawing or pushing of an electron beam from its normal course by an electromagnetic or electrostatic field.

Deflection plates—Plates in an oscilloscope C-R tube that deflect the beam. The vertical plates (vertically deflecting plates) are normally the ones to which the signal is applied; the horizontal plates deflect the beam for the horizontal sweep.

Display—The waveform appearing on the screen of a TV tube or scope.

Dynamic—Having power. Usually refers to conditions where AC signal power is present and to measurements made under such dynamic conditions, such as the amount the plate current changes for a given change in plate voltage. (Opposed to static or DC conditions where we might measure the plate current at a given plate voltage.)

E

Electromagnetic—Having to do with the magnetic field set

up around a wire or wires carrying current. (See electro-static.) An electromagnetic field is one that surrounds a current-carrying wire, inductance, or transformer.

Electron-ray tube—A tuning tube in which electron rays make a target fluoresce or stop fluorescing as a signal is tuned in; a "magic-eye" tube.

Electrostatic—Having to do with electric voltages, as opposed to electromagnetic. An electrostatic field surrounds a point or area of high voltage.

F

Field, field strength—The area around an electric source in which electrical effects can be detected. Thus, one's hair may stand on end in the electrostatic field near a million-volt static generator. The hairspring of a watch may be magnetized in the electromagnetic field near a large inductor (or more commonly in the magnetic field near a speaker magnet).

Filter—Electronic or mechanical circuit or device that removes certain frequencies from the alternating current passing through it. May attenuate low frequencies, as a phonograph rumble filter; high frequencies, as in old-type tone controls, or block everything but a small band of frequencies (bandpass filter or trap).

Flat—Said of an amplifier or generator output that remains constant over a specific range of frequencies. ("The amplifier is flat from 20 to 20,000 Hz.").

Flying spot—A device used instead of a television camera. A very bright spot of light that sweeps across the scene being televised, scanning the field in exact synchronism with the television transmitter. The "camera" is a photocell, which picks up the illumination at the spot being scanned, and thus transmits a signal that varies exactly with the light and shade along the scanning line.

Form—Said of electrolytic capacitors. To build up the

active layer on the plates of an electrolytic capacitor after it has been idle for a long time. Usually done by placing the capacitor across DC at its working voltage for a short period.

Fundamental—Said of an electric wave with harmonics. The main or principal signal, to which all the harmonics are due.

G

Generator—In electronics, a producer of electric waves, such as an audio generator, an RF generator. In electricity, a mechanical producer of current, AC or DC.

Grid-dip oscillator—An instrument containing an oscillator with a meter in its grid (or equivalent) circuit. When brought into resonance with an external circuit, the meter reads lower, or "dips."

Grommet—A ring of insulating material used to protect conductors passing through an abrasive partition.

G - Y—See B - Y.

H

Harmonic—1. A multiple of a given frequency which is called the fundamental. The second harmonic of 100 Hz is 200 Hz; 300 Hz is the third harmonic. (The fundamental is itself the first harmonic.) 2. A signal at one of the harmonic frequencies—usually unwanted but sometimes—as in music—desirable and necessary.

Hertz (Hz)—Cycles per second: "a frequency of 60 Hz." formerly abbreviated (incorrectly) in the United States as c or cycles, and (correctly) in Britain as cps kHz; kilohertz, 1,000 Hz; MHz: Megahertz, 1 million Hz.

Heterodyne—The action of one signal on another signal at a different frequency. In an amateur receiver, a frequency of 456 kHz may be heterodyned with the 455-kHz IF to produce a 1,000-Hz note in the phones; in a TV receiver, a

carrier of 55.25 MHz is <u>heterodyned</u> with an internally produced frequency of 101 MHz to produce the 45.75-MHz IF.
See Superheterodyne.

<u>Hot</u>—Said of the conductor or element carrying the high volt-
age or the signal; the opposite end of a circuit from the <u>cold</u>,
or ground, end.

I

<u>IF, IFT</u>—Intermediate frequency, intermediate frequency
transformer.

<u>Impedance</u>—Opposition to the flow of electrons by the com-
bined resistance and reactance in a circuit. (See Resistance and Reactance.) Notice that the impedance is not the
arithmetic sum of the resistance and reactance: an impedance consisting of a resistor and capacitor in series, each
presenting 100 ohms to the circuit, will not have an imped-
ange of 200 ohms, but about 140. $Z = \sqrt{R^2 + X_C^2}$

<u>In-circuit</u>—Said of tests in which a component is checked
without disconnecting it from the equipment in which it is
used. Most often refers to transistor, capacitor, and resistor checkers, though technicians routinely check resistors
in a circuit with an ordinary ohmmeter.

<u>Intermodulation</u>—The effect of a signal of one frequency
acting on a signal of a different frequency. Generally encountered as distortion in audio amplifiers, but can occur
at radio frequencies ("station-riding").

<u>Isolation</u>—Separation of an electric circuit from another,
or a piece of equipment from the supply voltage as by an
<u>isolation transformer.</u>

K

<u>Keyed</u>—Controlled by a special signal transmitted regular-
ly, either from the transmitting station or a local source,
as the crystal oscillator of a rainbow generator.

L

Line—1. The trace on a CR tube screen; used especially in television. 2. The electric power supply line, as line voltage.

Linearity—The condition in which equal increases or decreases in input to a device or element produces equal increases or decreases in output. An amplifier stage is linear if, for example, an increase of 1 millivolt input produces an increase of 1 volt output. If above 15 kHz, an input increase of 1 mv produces less than 1 volt output, the amplifier is linear to 15 kHz.

Load—The circuit or device that receives or dissipates the power put out by a piece of equipment or circuit element. The speaker is the load for an amplifier; the air in the room loads the speaker. A tube's plate load may be a resistor or a transformer winding.

Loop—A coil of several or many turns of wire wound or spaced on a frame used to pick up a signal. Loops may vary from about half an inch in diameter (as needed in signal tracing for hum pickup to many feet for direction-finding antennas. Also used as a ferrite antenna, which is a close-wound coil rather than a loop.

M

Marker—A sharply tuned and accurately calibrated signal that indicates a known frequency, usually on the response curve made by a sweep generator.

Mixer—1. The element (tube, transistor, diode) that combines a received signal with one generated locally (within the receiver) and puts out a third signal, usually a sum or difference frequency of the two input signals. See converter. The terms mixer and converter have been used loosely and interchangeably by some authors. 2. (Usually encountered in audio). A circuit that combines two or more separate signals into one. A microphone mixer, for example, may combine the output of two or several microphones.

Multi-meter—Usually applied to a combination voltmeter; (milli) ammeter and ohmmeter, though a multi-meter may have additional functions, such as decibel or capacitance measurements.

Multiplex—The process of sending several signals over one circuit, or on one carrier wave, simultaneously. In servicing, it usually refers to the sending of stereo signals plus, occasionally, a commercial broadcast on one FM carrier wave.

N

NTSC—National Television Standards Committee. The set of standards adopted by that committee, now used in U.S. color TV broadcasting.

O

Oscillator—Circuit or equipment that produces waves or alternating current (audio oscillator, the oscillator in a radio transmitter or superheterodyne receiver.).

P

Padder—A trimmer capacitor used at the maximum capacitance end of a variable capacitor's rotation in series with the variable capacitor. 2. An alignment adjustment at the low-frequency end of a tuning range. 3. (attenuator pad) A combination of resistors that may be inserted into a circuit to attenuate the signal by a known amount.

Parasites—Oscillations produced spontaneously in a circuit having no specific frequency relationship with the frequencies the circuit is designed to produce or handle. Parasites (or parasitics) in a radio transmitter usually occur at much higher frequencies than the desired one, and may waste power, distort signals, or burn out equipment. Parasites in audio equipment may appear in the audio range

(Howling or Whistling), above it (unheard and detectable only by their effects), or below it (motorboating or breathing).

Peak-to-peak—The measurment of an alternating voltage from its extreme positive excursion to its extreme negative one. The power line—rated at 120 volts effective (RMS)— swings from a positive 170 volts to an equal negative value. Thus the p-p voltage is about 340.

Phase—The portion of an AC waveform being discussed; the position of a signal on the AC wave. Any phenomenon that recurs or repeats regularly is measured in cycles of 360°. Thus the beginning of an AC wave of 60 Hz (1/60 second period) at 0 voltage is 0°. At its positive peak, 1/240 seconds later is at 90°. It drops to zero again at 180° (1/120 seconds) reaches its negative peak at 270° (3/240 seconds) and is back to zero again at 360° (or 0°) in 1/60 second. Two AC currents or signals are in phase if they reach the same points throughout their cycle simultaneously; out of phase if they do not. The voltage in an AC wave is in phase with the current if it reaches peaks and zero points at the same time the current does.

Phase modulation—A form of modulation in which the intensity (or hue) of the signal varies with the difference between its phase and that of the carrier. Roughly similar to frequency modulation.

Pip—A small sharp vertical indication on the scope trace.

Post injection—Mixing a marker signal with the sweep generator signal after it has gone through the TV IF.

Potentiometer, pot—Originally a measuring device in which the voltage to be measured is balanced against a reference voltage. Now applied indiscriminately to any variable resistor with three terminals. (Notice that the scientific instrument is never called a "pot" but that the variable resistor is often called a potentiometer.)

Power factor—The ratio of the power (watts) in a circuit to the volt-amperes. This depends on the ratio of resistance to reactance. A pure resistance has a power factor of 1; a pure reactance, 0. When a capacitor begins to absorb power its <u>power factor</u> rises and the capacitor becomes progressively less useful as the power factor increases.

<u>Pre-injection</u>—The insertion of a marker signal with the sweep generator signal at the input of a TV IF amplifier.

<u>Pulse</u>—1. An electrical impulse of very short duration. 2. The vertical line produced on the scope screen by such an impulse.

R

<u>Rainbow</u>—The pattern made on the screen of a TV receiver by a generator operating 1,750 Hz below the color subcarrier frequency. All the colors appear in undefined vertical bars with the colors blending into each other at the edge of each bar. <u>Rainbow generator.</u> A color-bar generator producing a rainbow-type display.

<u>Raster</u>—The rectangle traced out by the horizontal and vertical sweeps on a picture tube screen, whether unmodulated (blank raster) or modulated (TV picture).

<u>Reactance</u>—The opposition offered to electron flow by a capacitance or inductance. Measured in ohms, like resistance, but unlike resistance, consumes no power. A reactance stores up the power as the AC voltage rises on an alternation, returns it as the voltage drops toward zero, then starts storing power on the next alternation.

<u>Resistance</u>—Opposition offered to electron flow by a less-than-perfect conductor. The power measured by the voltage drop across and current through the resistance is turned into heat. Thus, a resistance draws power from the circuit.

<u>Resistor string</u>—A number of resistors connected in series, commonly as a voltage divider or multiplier in a VOM or VTVM.

<u>Return</u>—The conductor that connects one end of a circuit to the common or ground conductor. Thus, the lead from the cold end of the grid coil is the <u>grid return.</u>

<u>RF, RFT</u>—Radio frequency, radio frequency transformer.

<u>RMS</u>—Root-mean-square, so called from the method of calculating it. The effective value of an AC voltage or current—the voltage and current that would produce the same amount of heat in a resistor as a given DC voltage and currents.
<u>R-Y</u>—See B-Y.

S

<u>Scanning line</u>—1. The (normally horizontal) line traced out by the sweep circuit of an oscilloscope or a TV picture tube. 2. The time occupied by a scanning line, as "the keyed rainbow generator operates at a frequency <u>one scanning line</u> lower than the picture subcarrier."

<u>Screen</u>—1. The phosphor-coated face of a scope CR tube or TV picture tube on which the electron trace or image appears. 2. The screen-grid or shield-grid element of an electron tube. 3. A metal shield that protects components within it from an electromagentic or electrostatic field.

<u>Shield</u>—A protective metallic screen that protects anything within or behind it from the effect of electric fields, as a <u>shielded cable.</u>

<u>Shunt</u>—An additional circuit in parallel with the principal one. A meter shunt may carry 9/10 of the current in a circuit, while the main path through the meter carries only 1/10. (<u>In shunt,</u> or <u>in shunt with:</u> connected across).

<u>Signal substituter</u>—A device that produces a signal that can be used to service a piece of equipment in place of the signal the equipment was designed to handle. A signal generator is the most common type of signal substitute. The term is often applied to a complete TV receiver from which RF, IF or video signals can be switched into a defective set. Even sparks from a plastic comb have been used as a signal substitute.

<u>Signal tracer</u>—A piece of test equipment used to pick up radio or audio signals at different points in a receiver. It nor-

mally has probes for RF and AF pickup. The scope is the instrument normally used for TV signal tracing.

Sine wave—An electrical quantity (voltage or current) that varies according to the law of sines. An excellent example is a mark on the rim of a wheel rolling along the ground. The distance from the ground to the mark at any point in the wheel's rotation is equivalent to the amplitude of the electrical quantity at the same point in the cycle—at 45°, for example, the distance (voltage) is 0.707 of maximum amplitude. Sine-wave current is the type produced by rotating machinery and many types of static generators.

Spectrum—A specific range of frequencies. The audio spectrum covers frequencies from about 20 to 20,000 Hz.

Spot—The dot of light projected on the face of a CRT by the electron beam. If the beam moves, the spot becomes a trace or line.

Square wave—An electrical signal that rises very rapidly from zero to full amplitude, remains there throughout the whole duration of the wave, then drops rapidly to zero and to a peak in the opposite direction. Usually produced by a combination of alternating currents of different frequencies.

Static—(Latin: standing) 1. Anything immobile. 2. Tests, etc., made under unchanging DC or no-signal conditions. The static characteristics of a tube include the amount of plate current it passes with a given plate voltage and grid voltage. 3. Atmospherics, electrical noise.

Subcarrier—A signal that modulates a carrier wave and can itself be modulated by a program other than the one on the main carrier. For example, the wave of an FM broadcast station, centered on 100 MHz, may be modulated by the main FM program for the first 15 kHz from center frequency by a pilot signal at 19 kHz, and by a subcarrier 30-kHz wide, centered 38 kHz from the center frequency of 100 MHz. This sub-band carries the L-R signal necessary for stereo broadcasting. There may be another subcarrier 14-kHz wide, centered at 67 kHz, for "storecasting."

Superheterodyne—A method of communications reception (or more correctly, amplification) in which the signal is heterodyned with an internally-generated signal to produce a heterodyne frequency above the audio range (supersonic or ultrasonic). Originally the heterodyne (intermediate frequency) was just above the audio range—usually 30 kHz—but was soon raised to 100 kHz, and now may be as high as 45 MHz in TV receivers.

Swamping resistors—A resistor connected across a tuned circuit to broaden its tuning range (at the cost of reducing its amplification).

Sweep—The regular movement of the beam across the face of a CR (scope or picture) tube. Generally called "horizontal sweep," but in some cases other sweeps, such as circular, may be used.

Sweep circuit or circuitry—The circuits that supply the voltage or power to deflect the beam across the face of a scope tube or TV picture tube.

Sync—(Abbreviation for synchronization) Making two things happen at the same time. Specifically the process (or circuitry) used to keep the received television signal synchronized with the transmission from the TV station.

T

Tolerance—The amount of deviation from the normal or rated value that may be permitted. A deviation of 10% from nominal values is permitted in most of the resistors and capacitors in TV sets. Broadcast stations must keep within 20 Hz of their assigned frequencies, a tolerance of 20 cycles per second.

Trace—The line of light sweep out on the face of a CR (scope or TV) tube by the electron beam. Usually called a line in TV.

Tunnel dipper—A dip meter that uses a tunnel diode as its oscillator instead of a tube or transistor.

Trimmer—Usually a small variable capacitor connected across a larger one to facilitate alignment. Sometimes applied to the variable ferrite cores of RF and IF coils. Trimmer resistors are used in industry, and at least one radio set had inductive trimmers on air-core coils.

U

Ultrasonic—1. Sound waves above the high-frequency end of the human hearing range. May start at about 15 kHz with no upper limit. 2. Electric waves just above the audio range—roughly, the frequencies between 15 and 30 kHz, though much higher frequencies are sometimes spoken of as ultrasonic.

V

Vernier—Strictly, a device mounted on dials to read small differences in rotation, usually down to a tenth of a scale division. Less correctly, but much more commonly, applied to any slow-motion tuning device.

Vestigial sideband—A method of reducing the bandwidth of a signal without running into the difficulties of single-sideband operation. One sideband is transmitted in full, while the other is attenuated greatly. In U.S. TV standards, the upper sideband extends 4.5 MHz from the carrier; the lower (vestigial) sideband only 1.25 MHz.

Voice—Used in connection with electronic organs to denote an output tone in which the fundamental and harmonics have been combined in such proportions as to give a desired effect, usually to imitate the voices of a standard pipe organ.

Voltage doubler—A circuit (usually, but not always, a power supply) that receives AC at a given voltage and puts out DC at roughly double the voltage.

Voltage multiplier—A string of resistors that extends the range of a voltmeter. With a voltage multiplier the range of a meter that would normally read full scale with a voltage, say, of 60 millivolts, can be extended almost without limit, often to 5,000 volts in practical service instruments.

Z

Zero-set— The adjustment that sets the pointer of a meter exactly at zero. The act of making the adjustment (to "zero-set" the meter).

Index

DATE DUE